JUNIOR COLLEGE DISTRICT
of St. Louis - St. Louis County
LIBRARY
7508 Forsyth Blvd.
St. Louis, Missouri 63105

  PRINTED IN U.S.A.

COMPUTER CIRCUIT PROJECTS
you can build

by **LEE BOSCHEN**

HOWARD W. SAMS & CO., INC.
THE BOBBS-MERRILL CO., INC.
INDIANAPOLIS · KANSAS CITY · NEW YORK

FIRST EDITION

FIFTH PRINTING — 1967

Library of Congress Catalog Card Number: 63-15844

Preface

Electronic computers have burst on the American scene with all the impact of a 4th of July roman candle. Editorials have been written in their behalf, and cartoonists have had a field day drawing monstrous machines covered with dials, levers, and slots marked IN and OUT. Science fiction writers have imagined worlds in which computers either controlled every act of human beings, or were mere slaves to the whims of humans.

Yet in spite of all this outpouring, very little has been done to show what computers are *really* like . . . how they operate, and the principles on which they function. And even less effort has been expended to bring these principles to the home experimenter and electronics hobbyist.

This book is intended to do just that—to give a glimpse into the fascinating world of computer technology. Many of the principles will be familiar to the experienced electronic hobbyist, although the applications of these ideas may be somewhat more novel.

I am a firm believer in the theory that what you learn with your hands you don't forget, and you'll find a lot here to do with your hands. It is my earnest hope that you will continue reading, building, and experimenting with computer circuits. Perhaps you, too, can make a contribution to this fascinating field, if you really try.

LEE BOSCHEN

April, 1963

To Edward Meadows

Contents

CHAPTER 8

CHAPTER 9

CHAPTER 10

CHAPTER 11

CHAPTER 12

CHAPTER 13

CHAPTER 14

CHAPTER 15

CHAPTER 1

Parts, Tools and Techniques

"Where can I get the parts?" is a cry familiar to everyone who has tried to construct anything electronic or electrical in nature. And indeed the problem can be very real, especially where the parts needed are special, or are very old or new. Although this will not be of concern in these projects (most of the really computer-designed parts used are in such tremendous production that they are readily available, and their cost has been brought to quite reasonable levels for such high-quality components), some discussion of parts supplies is in order.

You will notice 150 volts is the highest voltage used in the tube circuits, while 25 volts is the highest DC potential in the transistor circuits. What, then, is the proper voltage rating of the parts for the projects? The answer in many cases depends on what you intend to do with the completed devices. If you wish to keep them intact, and put them to use, buy parts with a voltage rating that fits the circuit under consideration. If, on the other hand, you intend to disassemble the completed items and reuse the parts, buy components with ratings of at least 200 volts DC. This will permit you to use the components in both transistor and tube circuits. These ratings, by the way, indicate the voltage the component will withstand under normal operating conditions (test voltages are higher), and have a great deal to do with the price.

This is particularly true of electrolytic capacitors. If you try to go to either extreme—very small sizes, for example, with low voltage ratings for ultra-compact transistor devices, or higher voltage ratings (450 to 600 volts) for maximum safety and dependability—you will find that prices start to rise rapidly. So stay as close to 200 volts DC as you can without going under that value. This is a happy compromise for both safety and cost. The price variations of paper or ceramic capacitors dependent on voltage ratings aren't nearly so extreme, so in this case a higher voltage rating (400 volts) is recommended. In any event, the voltage ratings given in the parts lists for the various projects are satisfactory. One note of caution, however, should be stated in regard to the use of high-voltage capacitors in transistor circuits. An electrolytic capacitor rated at 600 volts may not "form" properly at only 6 or 12 volts, consequently the capacitance actually present in the circuit may be far less than the rated value. In fact, the value may be so much less than that which you believe you have that circuit operation may be radically altered or impaired.

As for resistors, use what you can get cheaply. Don't try too hard to find the small transistor resistors. While it's true that they can make a wonderfully compact electronic assembly, it is also true that you'll have to pay a higher price to get them. Miniaturization comes high! For example, ¼-watt resistors can cost as much as 25% more than the more common ½-watt size; hence if you get the latter, you are getting 100% more dissipation rating for 25% less money. Only the size is increased, and that will not be a problem in any of these projects.

As a matter of fact, if you can make it fit, a 1-watt or even a 2-watt resistor will be satisfactory in any application calling for a ½-watt resistor; you'll notice several places in these projects where this was done! Just don't try to go the other way, i.e., from 2-watt down to ½-watt size. How can you tell the difference in wattage rating? Simple—the larger the resistor, the higher the wattage rating.

Get to know your parts distributor. He can be a great help to you as you look for your best bargains in parts. He is familiar with a tremendous variety of components, and through his catalog ordering system, can get you literally anything you'll ever need in these projects or any others you may develop in the future. If you will ask for them, you can get copies of distributor's catalogs. These contain a wealth of information, and you can shop among them just as you would shop at the various stores.

Be especially watchful for sales that are held from time to time. Judicious shopping at special sales presents opportunities to get good parts at low prices (prices you can't match at other times) for components your distributor will stand behind.

And another thing, some of the distributing houses have special sales that present an almost unequalled opportunity to the experimenter to get good parts at low prices. A letter to several of the major parts-supply houses asking to be placed on their mailing list will keep you in touch with their sales, and solve a great many of the parts problems you'll likely encounter.

There is one parts source that should not be overlooked; try to secure an old (not *too* old, please) radio or television receiver from a neighbor or friend and carefully strip the parts from it. The voltage and wattage ratings of these components will probably be more than adequate for most of the projects outlined in this book. And you can't beat that price anywhere.

TOOLS

Just how much benefit can be derived from bargain tools is questionable. Of course, they don't cost as much initially, but they'll need to be replaced sooner. In these projects, very few tools will be needed; hence, if you buy the very best your investment will remain low, and if properly used the tools will last for many years.

The tools you will need are:

1. A small soldering iron, one of the pencil type, with approximately 40-watt size chisel tips that can be screwed into the iron.
2. A small pair of cutting pliers; *diagonals,* or *dikes,* as they are often called. The 4- to 5-inch size should serve very well.

3. A pair of needle-nosed pliers with very narrow tips (sometimes called *chain-nose* pliers). The 4½-inch size is recommended, although you may prefer a pair with longer handles, say, seven inches. Do not use them as wrenches and they will remain useful for many years. Be sure to get the kind without the cutting blades near the pivot end of the jaws—if you use this cutter-plier combination it's too easy to clip off a lead while trying to straighten it.
4. At least two screwdrivers; one with a 4-inch shank, and one with a 6-inch shank.
5. A hand drill for drilling holes in aluminum, useful in some of the projects. If you have an electric drill, so much the better.
6. A small rattail file for shaping holes.
7. A hand reamer with a ⅛-inch tip, and five or six inches in length.
8. Any of a variety of tools known as soldering aids. These are *most* useful in arranging parts or leads on the inside of a container, holding components which are to be soldered (be sure to get the type to which solder won't stick or you may end up soldering your tool into the circuit!), and as a scribe, a pointer, a pick, and an *un*-soldering aid. These tools have value far out of proportion to their cost, and are made in such a variety of styles that the purchase of more than one seems very reasonable.

TECHNIQUES

One of the most important factors in the success of any of these projects is the way the parts are soldered together. Soldering is very easy to do correctly; but unfortunately it is also very easy to do incorrectly. Perhaps the basic rule for good soldering is: put the solder on the work, not on the iron. Good soldering consists of the following steps:

1. Make good mechanical connections. Don't rely on the solder to hold the connection together.
2. Be sure the iron is properly tinned. It should be hot enough to melt solder instantly on contact with the iron.

The soldering-iron tip should be shiny with a thin film of solder before it is touched to the connection. This is very important.

3. Touch the soldering iron to the work, allow a *short* time for the connection to heat up, then touch the solder to the connection, *not* the iron. You will notice that when the solder melts it penetrates every part of the solder joint very quickly. Remove the iron at once and do not touch the joint until it has had time to cool. You can tell when a solder joint has cooled by watching it closely after you have removed the iron. As the joint cools, first around the edges and then to the center, a peculiar haze will seem to pass over the hot metal—very rapidly—after which the joint is cool enough, and strong enough, to stand movement.

4. Use only rosin core solder. If you have any doubt about the type of solder you have on hand, it is strongly recommended that you buy a new roll plainly marked ROSIN CORE RADIO SOLDER. There are a variety of suitable products of this nature on the market; Kester *Radio-TV Solder*, Ersin *Multi-core*, or similar types. Such solders are an alloy of tin and lead, a 60-40 (60% tin and 40% lead) mixture is recommended.

A half hour's practice with some scrap pieces of wire and an old tube socket might very well save you several hours of troubleshooting time when you start to work on the projects. Save these hours—be careful when soldering.

CIRCUIT ASSEMBLY

There is nothing sacred about the way these projects are arranged; if you want to use a different form of circuit layout, by all means feel free to do so. However, certain suggestions regarding parts are in order. On the first assembly of these projects, and possibly before you know whether you are going to leave the project assembled or whether you are going to tear them down . . . don't cut the leads to fit. If you ever hope to use the parts in any other type of circuit, and the leads are too short, you can grow gray trying to make things fit.

It's really amazing how leads can "shrink" after they have been cut to fit in a few different circuits.

TRANSISTORS

If you exercise reasonable care in the treatment of transistors, you will find that they have an extraordinarily long service life. Heat, as applied during soldering, will not injure them. Heat will, however, alter the performance of a transistor temporarily (permanently, if sufficiently overheated), at least while the transistor is warm. As a result of this heat, or thermal, sensitivity property of transistors, considerable care must be taken in the *design* of transistor circuits to secure proper operation over a varying temperature range.

Your chief concern with the transistors used in the projects in this book is whether or not they are wired into the circuits correctly, and the way to be sure is to refer frequently to the basing drawings shown in the schematic diagrams of each project. If you substitute transistors, be certain that you have the proper base diagram of the new transistor.

POWER SUPPLIES

For transistor circuits, batteries are ready-made power supplies. They come in a great variety of styles and sizes, so that the only problem is choosing what you want. Many batteries have several taps on them, and by a judicious selection of these taps you may obtain whatever voltage you need.

The life of batteries is the only real drawback to their use. If you intend to use batteries for any length of time, be certain that you buy only the heavy-duty type, for light batteries can be drained of their charge in a short time.

Supplies using the 115 volts AC from the commercial power lines can be easily constructed; however they are considerably more expensive initially than batteries, in most cases. To offset the expense is the virtually limitless life of such power supplies.

CHAPTER 2

Automatic Signal Flasher

Perhaps the most basic unit in modern computers is the multivibrator. It appears in a great variety of forms in every electronic digital computer currently being manufactured. Its circuit can be modified to operate at frequencies ranging from millions of cycles per second to less than one cycle per second.

The signal flasher (Fig. 2-1) described in this chapter operates at about two cycles, or flashes, per second. It uses the

Fig. 2-1. The automatic signal flasher.

13

see-saw property of the multivibrator to turn one (or two) lights on and off in regular rhythm. It can be used for a variety of purposes; e.g., generating an attention-getting emergency signal, as an advertising gimmick, even turning on and off the lights on your Christmas tree.

The flasher is completely portable. Small enough to be carried easily in one hand, it needs only a 12-volt DC source, such as an automobile battery, to operate anywhere, at any time, in any position.

CONSTRUCTION

In its basic form the flasher is built in an aluminum box 4 inches long, 2 inches wide, and 2¾ inches high. One 2N256A transistor (a 2N307 will work just as well) is mounted on each end of the box in the following manner:

1. Mark and drill the holes (with a $^{11}/_{64}$" or number 18 drill) in the box through which will pass the base (B) and emitter (E) pins. A mounting template is often furnished with new transistors and should be used as a guide when marking the holes for drilling. Otherwise, use the two pins or a base diagram (Fig. 2-2A) to mark the drilling positions.

2. Set the 2N256A on the box with the B and E pins centered in the holes (drilled in step 1). Mark the holes through which the transistor mounting screws will pass with a sharply pointed object (a straight pin will do) (Fig. 2-2B). These holes should be drilled large enough to admit the raised portion of a shoulder washer (approx. ¼") that will just pass a No. 6 screw (Fig. 2-2B).

To see if they fit, try mounting the insulating wafers (Fig. 2-2B) and transistors temporarily; the holes in the box should line up with the mounting holes in the transistors, and the B and E pins should have at least $^{1}/_{16}$" clearance all the way around. Before the two transistors are permanently mounted on the case, coat both sides of the insulating wafer (Fig. 2-2B) with a thin film of silicone grease (Dow Corning DC3 or DC4, G.E. Silicone Dielectric Grease, #SS-4005, or equivalent). This will greatly facilitate the transfer of heat from the transistor

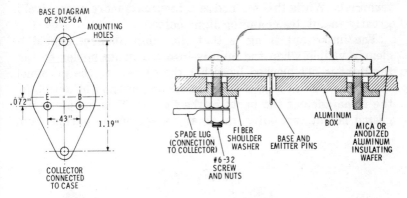

(A) Base diagram of power transistor.

(B) Power transistor mounting.

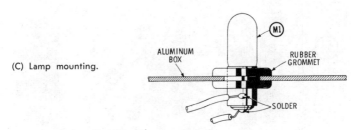

(C) Lamp mounting.

Fig. 2-2. Mounting methods.

collector to the flasher case, which will act as a heat sink to cool the transistor.

The next step is mounting the terminal strips and the light-bulb socket. The approximate location of the screws holding the terminal strips can be seen in Fig. 2-1, as can the position of the red cover over the light bulb.

The pilot-light assembly used in the original flasher (Fig. 2-3) is fairly expensive and need not be duplicated. It was used simply because it was "on hand." There are other ways to accomplish the same result for a lot less money. One of these is to use a rubber grommet through which the light bulb is forced, the connections being made directly to the base of the bulb (Fig. 2-2C). (Fig. 5-2 also shows how this can be done.)

Another possibility is that a pilot-light socket—a very simple and inexpensive bayonet-base type—could be inserted in the grommet; the connections can then be made to the socket terminals. While this method is a few cents more expensive, it greatly facilitates changing light bulbs.

The important thing is that the lamp filament should be clearly visible when the bulb is inserted in its holder so that the light is not blocked by either the socket, or the grommet.

A close look at Fig. 2-3 will show one method of arranging the remainder of the parts in the flasher. This is only a suggested layout; actually, the arrangement of the various com-

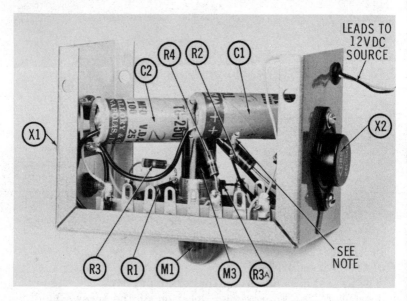

This is one way of making connections to the base and emitter pins of the 2N256A. Consult the text for further details.

Fig. 2-3. Internal view of chassis.

ponents is not in the least critical (as long as they are correctly wired into the circuit). If your components are shaped differently, you may want to use another mounting style.

Connections to the base and emitter pins of the 2N256A transistors can be made in any of several ways. You may solder directly to the pins, using a heat shunt (the tips of a pair of needle-nosed pliers) between the glass seals of the transistor and the soldering iron. Unless this is done, the heat may crack the glass seal and lead to early failure of the 2N256A.

16

You may also use a commercially manufactured transistor socket; Loranger Mfg. Corp, No. 2149, Cinch-Jones 2TS-1, or an equivalent, will be satisfactory for the 2N256A. Or you may make connecting fasteners from the pins of a seven or nine-pin miniature socket. The socket pins are removed from the socket by grasping them where they come through the base of the socket with a pair of needle-nosed pliers and forcing them back through the base. The pins will not pass through the base unless they are free of all solder and bits of wire that may have been soldered to them previously. Once the pins have been removed from the base of the socket, the leads to the base and emitter are soldered to them and they are slid onto the proper pins of the 2N256A. They will grip tightly, serving very well as connectors. Fig. 2-3 shows the final appearance of one such connection prior to being slid onto the 2N256A pins.

The flasher is very simple to use—merely make the power connections and that's all there is to it. If it is to be used in an automobile that has an electric plug-in cigarette lighter, a fitting that will substitute for the lighter can be fastened to the end of the power cord to make rapid connection possible. Be sure, when wiring the connector, to observe proper polarity.

Circuit Variations

Slower operation—There are a number of variations to the basic flasher circuit which you may find useful. For instance, if you want the flasher to operate much more slowly, and with longer flashes (about 1½ seconds), then you need merely unsolder the end of resistor R1 which goes to the negative (−) terminal of the battery and resolder it to the junction of R3 and capacitor C1. The battery end of resistor R2 should be unsoldered and moved to the junction of M1 and C2. That's all there is to it.

Two lights—Another very simple change that can be made in the flasher is the use of a second light bulb. To make this change you need only remove resistor R3, and in its place solder another No. 44 light bulb. You may wish to put longer leads on this lamp so that you can get some separation between the two lights; this has been found to increase the attention-getting value of the unit. Three or four feet separation should be enough, although you may use more or less to suit your special need. Incidentally, you need not feel that you are restricted to simple pilot lights in this flasher application. If you wish, you can remove resistor R4, and use a 12-volt bulb drawing as much as 1 ampere of current. In this case, however, the power source will need to be much huskier than with simple pilot lamps, although your automobile battery will still be adequate. *Also, use a 2N307 for this heavier current.*

Relay—One way to greatly increase the utility of the basic flasher is to use a relay in place of the lamp M1 and resistor R4 combination. The coil of the relay is wired into the circuit just as though it were a lamp, with one very special addition; a diode (e.g., 1N91) *must* be added across the coil to prevent the high-voltage pulses, generated by the collapsing field across the relay coil when it is turned off, from destroying the transistor. The diode must be wired so that the arrow on its case points in the direction of the 2N256A collector terminal.

Any 12-volt DC relay having a coil resistance of 50 ohms, or so, should work very well. Depending on the current rating of the relay points, large loads can be turned on and off by this device—lights, gongs, sirens, etc. This particular modification works especially well in conjunction with the slower-operation change described earlier.

Parts List

Item	Description
C1, C2	100-mfd, 25 VDC electrolytic capacitor
R1, R2	2,200-ohm, 1-watt resistor
R3	47-ohm, 1-watt resistor
R3A, R4	15-ohm, 1-watt resistor
X1, X2	2N256A transistor
M1	No. 44 pilot lamp; 6 to 8 volt, 250 ma
M2	12-volt battery
M3	pilot-light socket assembly
Misc.	terminal strips (2), wire, screws and nuts, No. 6 shoulder washers (4), rubber grommets, *Minibox* (Bud CU-2115-A or equivalent), and two transistor insulators—either .002-inch mica, or anodized aluminum wafers.

MULTIVIBRATOR CIRCUITS

The term multivibrator (MV) has come to mean a two-stage amplifier with positive feedback; it is usually found in one of three forms:

1. Astable—a free-running oscillator in which each tube or transistor conducts alternately at a frequency determined by the time constant of the cross-coupling elements, as RtCt in Fig. 2-4A. This type of multivibrator is used in modern computers as a square wave and timing pulse generator and for frequency division. It can be synchronized to operate at sub-multiples of its normal free-running frequency.

In high-speed digital computers this circuit operates at frequencies of one-million cycles per second, or even higher. It is this high initial frequency that enables a computer to do so much in such a short time; e.g., at 1,000,000 cps, a complete cycle can be completed in 1 microsecond (1/1,000,000 second).

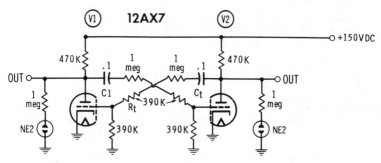

Rt is the sum of the 1 megohm-390K-390K resistors in series. They are divided in this circuit to secure proper operating voltages, timing conditions, and waveforms.

(A) Circuit diagram.

(B) V2 grid voltage waveform.

(C) V2 plate voltage waveform.

Fig. 2-4. Vacuum-tube multivibrator.

19

In a few such cycles a complete addition or subtraction can take place.

2. Monostable—a form of multivibrator which has but one stable state. Normally, in this circuit one of the tubes or transistors conducts continuously and the other remains cut off. When triggered, a monostable multivibrator will switch to its unstable state; it will remain there for a length of time determined by the time constant of the *AC* cross-coupling network. The other network is a *DC* coupling that can hold the circuit in one state indefinitely—or until a trigger pulse causes a change.

This circuit is widely used as a means of securing delayed pulses or generating standardized pulses from random-width trigger pulses.

3. Bistable—a form of multivibrator that has *two* stable states. It is sometimes called a *flip-flop*. When triggered, the

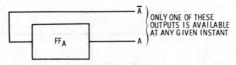

Fig. 2-5. Block diagram of flip-flop.

bistable multivibrator changes from one stable state to another and remains in the new state until triggered again, so that of the two possible outputs, first one and then the other is available. (An output is the presence of some specified voltage.) In Fig. 2-5, flip-flop A shows the two outputs; if the flip-flop is on, output A is available, if the flip-flop is off, output $\overline{A}$ (not A) is present. In properly operating flip-flop you can never have outputs A and $\overline{A}$ present at the same time. Perhaps the most common of the three types of multivibrators, the bistable is useful as a form of binary storage, a gate generator, and as a counter.

Vacuum-Tube MV Operation

In Fig. 2-4A, because of tube unbalance, small differences in component values, etc., one tube will always conduct more heavily than the other. The plate voltage on this tube (e.g., V1) will drop because of its 470K plate resistor, causing a negative voltage shift to appear, via the AC cross-coupling network, at the grid of V2 (Fig. 2-4B). This shift appears because as the voltage drops at the plate of V1, capacitor C1 discharges through the series 1-meg–390K–390K resistor combination to ground, then back up through V1 to the other side of C1. This negative grid voltage reduces V2 plate current and causes the plate voltage to rise (Fig. 2-4C). This rise is reflected back to the grid of V1 through the other AC cross-coupling network (CtRt). This positive-shift signal causes V1 to conduct harder and its plate voltage to drop even lower. This process continues until V2 plate current is cut off and V1 is conducting to saturation.

At this point no more signals are coupled through the networks; i.e., capacitor C1 continues to discharge through the 1-megohm–390K–390K resistor combination, but no shift of voltage is taking place on either plate. The circuit will remain in this state until the charge on coupling-timing capacitor C1, which holds the grid of V2 below cutoff, discharges to the point where V2 can begin to conduct (Fig. 2-4B). Once again the cross-coupling of signals begins, only this time in reverse; the drop in plate voltage, as V2 begins to conduct, appears on the grid of V1 as a negative-going signal. Therefore V1 will conduct less and its plate voltage will rise . . . and so on until V1 is cut off and V2 is conducting to saturation, and a complete cycle has been accomplished. This see-saw operation will continue at a frequency determined by the time constant of the AC cross-coupling networks, the supply voltage, and the tube type. The signal, in the form of a square wave (Fig. 2-4C), can be taken off either plate; each signal will be exactly 180° out of phase with the other.

Transistor MV Operation

In Fig. 2-6, two PNP transistors are connected in a common-emitter configuration to form a free-running multivibrator. As in the vacuum-tube circuit, due to various circuit parameters one of the transistors will conduct more than the other (e.g., X1). Hence, because of M1 and R4 the X1 collector voltage will rise toward zero, or ground (Fig. 2-7), and capacitor C2 will discharge through the X1 collector-emitter circuit, the battery, and R2, reverse-biasing the X2 base-emitter cir-

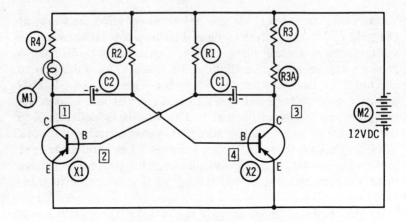

Fig. 2-6. Signal flasher circuit diagram.

cuit past cutoff. As capacitor C1 charges through the X1 base-emitter circuit, the battery, and R3, it adds forward-bias current to the X1 input, driving its collector current into saturation. At this point X2 is cut off and X1 is conducting to saturation.

As capacitor C2 continues discharging, its voltage becomes less (and the base of X2 becomes less positive) until, at a

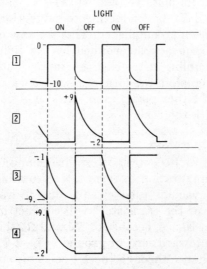

Fig. 2-7. Operating waveforms of circuit shown in Fig. 2-6.

point near zero volts, X2 forward-bias current begins flowing (through R2) and X2 starts to conduct. As X2 does so, its collector voltage rises toward ground (because of the drop across R3 and R3A) and capacitor C1 begins to discharge through the X1 collector-emitter circuit, the battery, and R1. The flow of electrons in the X1 input circuit is such that reverse bias is applied to the base-emitter circuit, tending to cut off collector current. Capacitor C2 is recharged through R4 and the X2 base-emitter circuit in such a manner that the forward bias of X2 is increased, and X2 collector current increases to saturation at the same time as X1 is cut off—just the reverse of the previous condition (Fig. 2-7). As in the vacuum-tube circuit, this alternation will continue at a frequency controlled by the time constant of the AC cross-coupling networks, the battery potential, and the transistor type.

CHAPTER 3

A Rally Computer

The rally computer to be described is a vacuum-tube application of a multivibrator circuit that sports-car enthusiasts can put to use during the next rally. It is also of value to cross-country drivers who wish to maintain a particular *average* speed under conditions where the speed at any given instant might vary, as in mixed city and country driving.

Essentially a counter, the computer counts intervals of distance as a function of time. The basis of the computer is the formula:

$$D = T \times R$$

where,
   D is distance in miles,
   T is time in hours,
   R is rate in miles per hour.

The rally computer continuously makes calculations according to this formula and presents the constantly changing answers in easily read form on a mechanical counter. As long as the driver keeps the readings of his automobile odometer and the rally computer identical, he knows that he is averaging the speed to which the computer dial is set, for example (Fig. 3-1), 32 mph.

The rally computer is valuable because it relieves the driver (or his navigator) of the wearisome task of making constant time and distance calculations, hence enabling them to con-

Fig. 3-1. Rally computer.

centrate on the road and the rally instructions. However, this computer is not magical, it can merely furnish a set of figures to serve as a guide to the driver and navigator. If the driver gets lost, all the computers in the world won't help.

CONSTRUCTION

The rally computer is constructed in a $4 \times 5 \times 6$-inch aluminum box. The mounting locations of the tube sockets, Counter Advance push-button switch (M2), Power On indicator lamp (M3), octal power plug (M5), and fuse holder (M4) can be seen in Fig. 3-2. The *mph* control (R4) is located on the front of the box; the three holes spaced above and to the sides of the R4 shaft are used in mounting the dial. Two of these holes are shown in use in Fig. 3-1; the third is covered by the dial pointer.

The locations of the other components are shown in Fig. 3-3. Resistors R2, R3, and R5 cannot be seen—they are hidden beneath C1. Capacitor C3, mounted on the sidewall of the box opposite R4, is a "junkbox" component—rather than spend time and money trying to duplicate this capacitor, you can use a 1.0-mfd electrolytic capacitor with a voltage rating of not

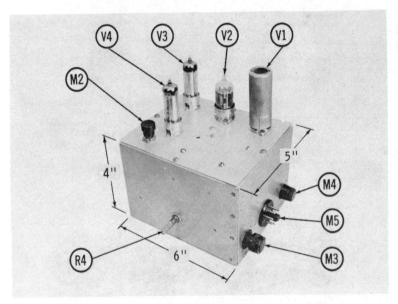

Fig. 3-2. External view of computer with dial removed.

less than 200 volts DC. The positive (+) lead of the capacitor should be connected to pin 1 of V1A.

Power On indicator-lamp holder M3 is not essential to the operation of the computer—it is a war-surplus lamp assembly used in the original computer as a blown-fuse indicator as well as a power-on light.

When you construct the rally computer, note that circuit returns are not connected to the chassis, but rather to a common ground bus. With this arrangement the device can be used in automobiles having either a positive or a negative ground system, and the box can be grounded to the frame

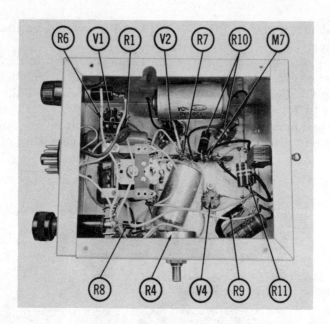

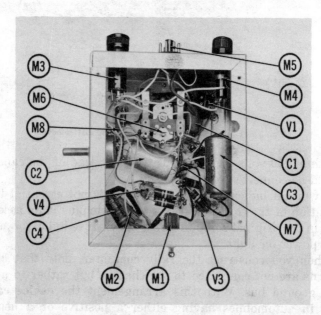

Fig. 3-3. Bottom views of computer chassis showing parts layout.

if desired. The grounded side of the automobile battery should be connected to pin 3 of the octal plug which fits onto M5. The connections in the diagrams (Figs. 3-5 and 3-6B) are shown for a positive ground system. If your system has a negative ground (most American cars do), be sure to make changes where necessary.

The Dial and Mounting Board

The dial is made large (Fig. 3-4) for quick and easy reading. Also, the dial pointer is fashioned so that it can be quickly adjusted and solidly clamped into place by a spring clip such as that shown in Fig. 3-1.

The board on which the rally computer and its power supply are mounted (Fig. 3-1) owes its odd shape to the fact that it was cut to fit in the left rear seat of a 1958 Austin-Healey. Note the angle at which the computer is fastened to its mounting; the dial is readily accessible to a person in the right front seat. Accessibility is one of the most important factors you must consider when you design a mounting base to fit your own car.

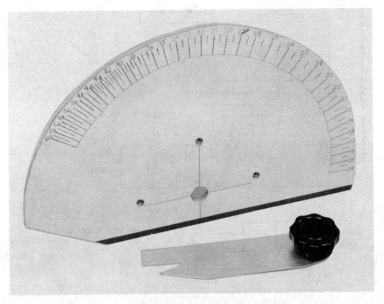

Fig. 3-4. Dial and pointer.

Power Supply

The power supply (Heathkit vibrator type, Model VP-1-12 or equivalent) furnishes 260 volts DC to the octal power plug, as shown in Fig. 3-5. If your car has a radio receiver that can

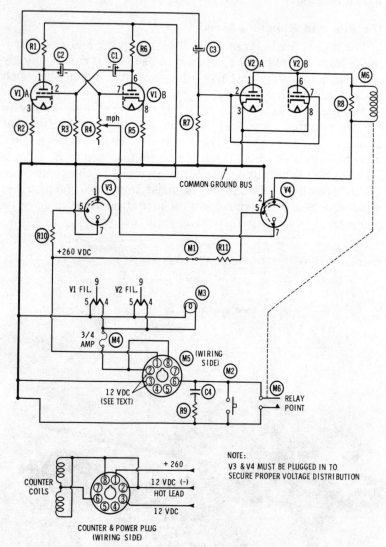

NOTE:
V3 & V4 MUST BE PLUGGED IN TO
SECURE PROPER VOLTAGE DISTRIBUTION

Fig. 3-5. Rally computer circuit.

furnish a similar voltage, it can be used instead of this supply, provided the B+ lead can be shifted from the radio receiver to the rally computer. Trying to use both the radio and the computer at the same time might place too heavy a load on the receiver power supply. If the output voltage of the radio power supply differs widely from +260 volts, R10 and R11 may have to be changed to compensate.

The mounting location of the power supply is not critical; however, to prevent any short circuits or loss of filament voltage, substantial and well insulated wire should be used to carry the power to the computer.

Mechanical Counter

The counter used in the original computer is a five-position Veeder-Root electrical-impulse counter. Originally, this counter was designed for use with 40 volts DC; however, wiring the two magnet coils of the counter in parallel, instead of the series arrangement used by the manufacturer, permits the counter to operate quite well on only 12 volts DC. Several counters of this type, i.e., fairly low-resistance coils (40 to 100 ohms), have been tried with excellent results; so if you have access to such a counter, don't be afraid to experiment with it to make it work.

Counters are also available that will operate directly in the plate circuit of V2 (e.g., Sodeco TCe Z5E); if this type is used, relay M6, resistor R9 and capacitor C4 can be eliminated. Counter Advance switch M2 should be changed to a SPDT (single-pole double-throw) push-button switch of the momentary-contact type. Count Interrupt switch M1 is then moved to the cathode circuit of V2 (Fig. 3-6A).

If the operating voltage of the plate-circuit counter is less than 150 volts DC, a small-value dropping resistor must be connected in series with the counter. A four-position counter will be satisfactory. The total will be 99.99 miles before changing to 00.00. Information on such counters is available from Landis & Gyr, Inc., 45 W. 45th St., New York 36, New York. Another source of electromagnetic counters and information is Veeder-Root, Inc., 46 Sargeant Street, Hartford 2, Conn.

With the arrangement shown on Fig. 3-5 the leads to the counter coils are fastened to pins 6 and 8 of the plug that fits on M5. These counter leads can be as long as you wish, thus enabling you to place the counter where it can be most easily seen by the driver—no small safety consideration.

Parts List

Item	Description
C1, C4	.1 mfd, 400 VDC
C2	2.0 mfd, 400 VDC
C3	.8 to .9 mfd, 220 VAC (see text)
R1, R6, R8	100K, ½-watt resistor
R2, R5	390-ohm, ½-watt resistor
R3	2.2-meg, ½-watt resistor
R4	2.0-meg, ½-watt potentiometer
R7	1.2-meg, ½-watt resistor
R9	300-ohm, ½-watt resistor
R10	9.0K, 4-watt resistor (2 18K, 2-watt units in parallel)
R11	7.5K, 4-watt resistor (2 15K, 2-watt units in parallel)
V1	6211 twin-triode tube
V2	5965 twin-triode tube
V3, V4	OA2 voltage-regulator tube
M1	SPST switch
M2	normally-open push-button switch
M3	pilot light holder (surplus, see text)
M4	fuse holder
M5	octal plug, chassis mounting type
M6	10,000-ohm plate relay, see text
M7, M8	four-position terminal strip (i.e., 4 positions + grounds).
Misc.	Seven-pin miniature shield-base socket (2); nine-pin miniature shield-base socket (2).

CALIBRATION

Calibration of the rally computer consists essentially of adjusting the counting rate to agree with the automobile odometer. To find the *approximate* settings of the dial pointer (hence R4), you will need only a 12-volt source and a stopwatch. Connect the 12-volt power leads to the rally computer power supply and let the unit warm up for a few minutes. With Count Interrupt switch M1 closed, check for the following:

1. The computer counter is showing an ever-increasing number,
2. The counting rate can be varied by *mph* adjustment R4,
3. Count Interrupt switch M1 will stop the counter.

With Count Interrupt switch M1 open, the Counter Advance switch (M2) should cause the counter total to increase one digit for every depression of the push button.

With M1 open, reset the computer counter to zero. Make a trial setting of the dial pointer to the high-range end of the

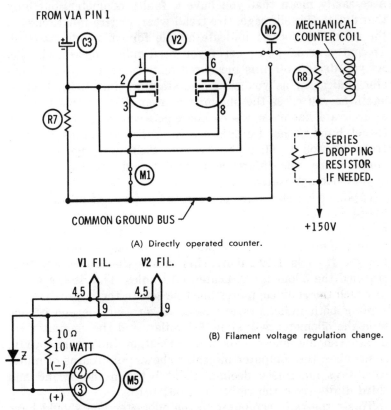

(A) Directly operated counter.

(B) Filament voltage regulation change.

Fig. 3-6. Supplementary diagrams.

dial, then close M1 and start the stopwatch at the same time. At the end of one minute, open M1 and read the number on the counter; if it is 00100, the computer is set for 60 mph; if it is 00050, the setting is 30 mph; and if the counter number is 00075, the computer is set to a speed of 45 mph.

The computer readings are in hundredths of a mile—ten miles will read as 01000, one mile will read as 00100, and $\frac{1}{10}$ mile as 00010—so that if at the end of one minute the counter indicates 00100, the computer is set for a rate of one mile per minute, or 60 mph.

One of the two problems involved in calibration is that of automobile odometer error. Virtually every odometer will show a slightly different reading for the same distance; this doesn't necessarily mean that you have a faulty odometer, but only that due to tire slippage, tire tread wear, or tire inflation, etc., the odometer doesn't indicate a mile for each mile traveled. To find your odometer error you need only a measured mile. As you drive over this measured distance, check your odometer indication as you cross the starting line, then check it again as you cross the one-mile marker. Record this reading as accurately as possible—estimate between the tenths of miles to get hundredths. Do this *several* times at speeds ranging from 20 mph to 60 mph. Average these readings to get a single figure. The difference between this figure and 1.00 mile is your odometer error.

If your odometer were perfect, the average of all the measured-mile figures would be 1.00 mile, meaning that for every mile actually traveled by the automobile, the odometer indicated one mile. However, assume that the figure obtained during the tests is 1.10 miles. This means that for every mile traveled the odometer indicates 1.10 miles. This is the figure to which the rally computer must be set. In the latter case, assuming both indicators are reset to zero, at the end of one mile the odometer will show 1.1 miles, and the computer indicator should show (for a five-position indicator) 00110. Remember, the computer indicator shows hundredths of miles, so always imagine a decimal point between the second and third digits from the right (i.e., 001.10).

To set the rally computer to the odometer you should have a stopwatch and someone to operate both it and the computer controls. This time, as you pass over the starting line of the measured mile, you must do so at a definite speed, such as 60 mph, and at the instant of crossover you should start the watch and close the computer Count Interrupt switch (M1). (The computer counter should have been reset to zero with the Count Interrupt switch open.) At the end of the measured mile stop the watch and open the Count Interrupt switch. If you averaged 60 mph, with the computer dial set correctly, then the watch should show one minute elapsed time, and the computer should indicate 00110 (assuming the odometer error mentioned earlier). If these are the readings you have, then make a mark on the computer dial to indicate the 60 mph setting and proceed to the next speed, e.g., 45 mph.

At 45 mph, using the same procedure, at the end of the measured mile, the watch should indicate 90 seconds and the counter should show 00110. At 30 mph the watch should show 120 seconds and the computer counter should again show 00110. This procedure should be repeated as many times as possible. When the calibration marks are drawn on the dial (Fig. 3-5), the speeds for which tests were not run can be estimated quite accurately by interpolation.

The only other possible problem involved in calibration is filament voltage regulation. This doesn't seem like much of a problem at first glance and really isn't, if the outlined calibration procedure is followed very carefully.

Filament voltage regulation is important because it affects the accuracy of the multivibrator. When the car is moving at a high speed, the generator voltage is likely to go as high as 14 volts, perhaps even higher. This voltage across the filament causes the cathode to boil off electrons at a greatly accelerated pace; the effect is as though the plate voltage had been increased. Hence, the charge and discharge times of the RC networks are changed. The rally computer will count faster for a given setting of the *mph* adjustment than if the filament were at its proper value. The degree to which this change of counting rate happens (at a given running speed) will vary slightly from run to run.

This is the reason you were advised to repeat the calibration procedure as many times as possible. However, should you wish to prevent voltage variations, you can do one of two things;

either use a separate 12-volt battery to run the rally computer, or make the change shown in Fig. 3-6B. A 10-watt, 6.8-volt zener diode (Hoffman 1N1805) should do for Z.

Using the Rally Computer

This is the simplest part of the entire project. Merely set the dial pointer to the speed you want to maintain as an average, and keep the computer counter and the automobile odometer readings the same by increasing or decreasing your speed. That's all there is to it, except . . . don't get lost!

CIRCUIT OPERATION

The theory of the multivibrator portion (V1A and V1B) of the rally computer is explained in Chapter 2; however, there are some additions. For example, the *mph* adjustment shown in Fig. 3-5 is used to vary the discharge time of C2, and thereby the frequency at which the multivibrator operates, or *counts*.

The 200-millisecond pulse output of V1A is coupled through C3 to the grids of V2A and V2B, wired in parallel. This coupling is accomplished by a flow of electrons from ground through R7, and into the negative terminal of C3. Electrons leave the positive terminal of C3 and pass through R1 on their path to the positive terminal of the power source. A negative shift is felt at the paralleled grids of V2 when electrons flow in the opposite direction; i.e., out of the negative plate of C3, through R7, to ground, then up through R2 and V1A (conducting) to the positive plate of C3. During positive pulses V2 conducts heavily through its plate load, relay M6; the resulting current pulse attracts the relay armature, thus closing the normally-open contacts. Twelve volts DC is thus applied to the counter magnet coils, causing the counter armature to rotate and mechanically operate the counter wheels.

When the voltage pulse on the V2 grids drops to zero the heavy current pulse through M6 ends, the relay drops out, and the counter armature is restored to normal, ready to receive the next pulse. In this manner, one count is added to the counter total for each multivibrator cycle at a rate controlled by *mph* adjustment R4.

CHAPTER 4

Simple
Stroboscope . . . Plus

This is a simple fun-type gadget that you can use to examine objects moving too fast to see with the unaided eye. It employs a different type of circuit than those mentioned earlier. Larger industrial versions are used to examine high-speed machinery and other rapidly moving objects. This simple adaption of the commercial stroboscope is sometimes used to test the response time of photocells. Other applications will doubtless suggest themselves as you become more familiar with the operation of this device. Several interesting variations (the reason for all the phono plugs at one end of the *Minibox*) are discussed later in the text.

The simple stroboscope employs a complementary symmetry DC amplifier, a circuit that is basically not frequency sensitive, being devoid of frequency-dependent components (i.e., capacitors and inductors). Such circuits are widely used in analog and digital computers because of the great range of pulse frequencies encountered.

The particular form of DC (direct coupled) amplifier used in the stroboscope offers the additional advantage of low power consumption—when no signal is present at the input, the current drain is less than 200 microamperes. This results from the simultaneous conduction and nonconduction of the transistors; either both on, 20+ ma, or both off, 200 μa.

CONSTRUCTION

Fig. 4-1 shows the general arrangement of the major components of the stroboscope. The parts should be set in place before any holes are drilled, because the compactness of the device does not leave much room for guessing. Indeed, it is strongly recommended that *all* the circuit components be assembled before the *Minibox* or other container is purchased, because the parts you have may be either larger or smaller than those shown in Fig. 4-2, thereby dictating a change in the size of the box from that given in the parts list.

In this respect, sharp-eyed readers may have noticed that the switch shown has several more than the five positions called for in the schematic diagram and the parts list. This particular switch (1-pole, 11 position) was bought at a "special" sale at the local parts distributor—a procedure outlined in Chapter 1. The switch is considerably larger than the usual five-position switch would be, but it is also much less expensive than usual.

Once the parts have been precisely located, their positions should be carefully marked and the mounting holes drilled. Close examination of Fig. 4-2 will show one possible parts arrangement; depending on the size and shape of your components, you may find other arrangements more satisfactory.

Fig. 4-1. The simple stroboscope.

One change you may wish to make in the stroboscope is the addition of a focusing reflector like those used in flashlights to concentrate the light pulses on whatever you wish to examine.

USING THE STROBOSCOPE

The operation of the stroboscope is simplicity itself; merely insert the shorting plug in M4 and the bulb-assembly plug in M2, connect the battery, and adjust the controls for an in-

Fig. 4-2. Internal view of stroboscope chassis.

termittent light of the desired frequency. If the bulb glows brightly without pulsing on and off, change the control settings until pulse operation is obtained, remembering that R1 controls the flash duration and R2 controls the period, or frequency, of the pulses. Misadjustment of the controls may result either in the lamp glowing continuously or remaining unlighted. Since there is considerable interaction between R1 and R2, some care must be taken to get the exact frequency you want.

At higher frequencies the lamp may appear to glow continuously, but dimly. This is because the eye, unable to follow the light pulsations due to persistence of vision, blends the short, rapid pulses together into a constant dim glow.

PLUS VARIATIONS

Although the unit was designed originally as a simple stroboscope, subsequent experimenting led to the discovery that the circuit could also be used for a wide variety of other purposes. For example, by judicious use of the shorting plug and the other plug-in units shown in Figs. 4-3 and 4-4 the device can be made to act as follows:

1. With M1 *off*, the relay assembly plugged into M2, the photocell assembly plugged into M4, and M5 open, the unit will act as a light-operated relay.

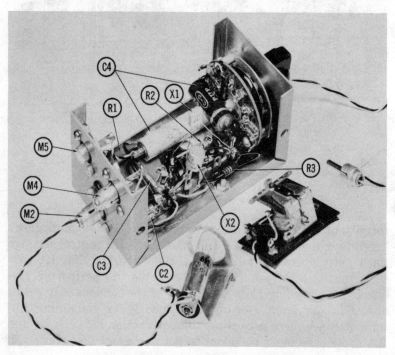

Fig. 4-3. Stroboscope chassis and external devices.

2. With M1 *off*, the transformer-speaker assembly inserted into M2, the shorting plug into M4, and the output of a crystal phono cartridge fed into M5, the unit will act as a phono amplifier.

3. With M1 in one of the Low-Range positions, the relay assembly plugged into M2, M4 shorted, and M5 open, the unit will act as a variable-frequency autocycling relay.

4. With M1 in the High-Range position, the transformer-speaker assembly connected into M2, M4 shorted, and M5 open, the unit will function as an audio oscillator suitable for learning and practicing the Morse code. With the .15-mfd capacitor used in the High-Range position, however, the tone heard from the speaker will be quite

Parts List

Item	Description
C1	10-mfd, 6-volt electrolytic capacitor
C2	2-mfd, 6 volt electrolytic capacitor (2 1-mfd capacitors in parallel)
C3	1-mfd, 6-volt electrolytic capacitor
C4	.15-mfd, 6-volt paper capacitor—made by wiring 2 (.1-mfd and .05-mfd) capacitors in parallel.
R1	1-meg, ½-watt potentiometer
R2	100K, ½-watt potentiometer
R3	This resistor is not used (it was removed after the photo was made as a result of further experiments).
X1	2N213 NPN transistor
X2	2N270 PNP transistor
M1	1-pole, 5-position rotary switch
M2, M4, M5	phono jack
M3	3-volt battery
Misc.	2¼ × 2¼ × 4-inch aluminum box (Bud CU-2103-A), knobs to fit ¼-inch shafts (3), light socket, six-position terminal strip, No. 49 light bulb, phono plugs (5) ; rubber grommet; screws and nuts, wire.

low in frequency. If you wish a higher-frequency range of tones, remove the .1-mfd capacitor from the M1 switch terminal, leaving the .05-mfd capacitor connected.

Remember any change in the values of capacitors C1 through C4 will affect the frequency range of the stroboscope the same way it affects the frequency range of the audio signal.

5. Using the arrangement of No. 4, except that the photocell assembly is plugged into M4, the unit will operate as a light-controlled oscillator, the frequency of which varies directly with the amount of light falling on the photocell.

6. Again using the same setup as No. 4, except that a resistor (100 to 200 ohms, 1 watt) is plugged into M2, the unit will act as a variable-frequency, variable-duration pulse generator. The signal is taken across the resistor. M1 may be in any of the four "active" positions; R1 and R2 are used to vary the pulse frequency and duration just as in the stroboscope.

Other variations are possible; combinations of inputs and outputs not considered in this chapter might very well prove

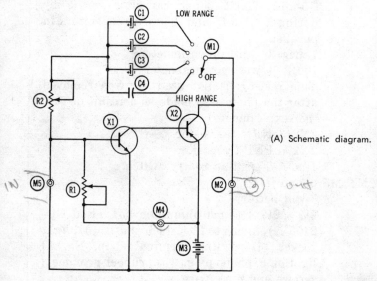

(A) Schematic diagram.

Fig. 4-4. Stroboscope

to be more than equal in interest and value to those which are mentioned here.

CIRCUIT OPERATION

The basic stroboscope circuit is a form of complementary-symmetry DC amplifier to which a feedback network has been added to cause regular cycles of operation. However, in some of the variations mentioned previously the feedback network (R2 and C1-C4) is omitted and the circuit operates as a high-gain amplifier.

For the sake of discussion, assume that the feedback network is open; i.e., M1 is in the off position (Fig. 4-5A). When the battery is connected, electrons flow from the negative terminal of the battery through the X1 emitter-base circuit, through R1, and to the positive terminal of M3. Unless R1 is

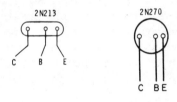

(B) Transistor base diagrams.

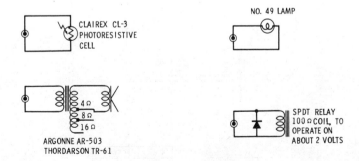

(C) External device diagrams.

circuit diagrams.

near its maximum value, consequently limiting the electron flow through X1, the current will forward-bias this NPN-type transistor; a negative-to-positive potential of about .2 volt appears between the X1 emitter and base. At this point the X1 emitter-collector resistance drops to a very low value and a negative potential is felt on the base of X2.

A negative potential on the base of PNP X2 will forward-bias this transistor. Its emitter-collector resistance approaches zero, and the battery voltage is impressed across M2, which lights. Hence, X2 acts as a switch, which is controlled by X1, and determines the brilliance of lamp M2.

The foregoing discussion has been based on the assumption that R1 was adjusted to a very low value of resistance. If, however, the value of R1 is increased, you will notice that the lamp will dim, going out completely at maximum resistance. This is because transistors are essentially current-amplifying devices. When the current into the base of X1 is limited (by increasing R1), the current into the base of X2 will also be limited, since it flows through X1. The electron path in this case is from the negative terminal of M3, through X1 emitter to base, then through a double circuit consisting of X2 base to emitter in parallel with R1, and back to M3 positive terminal. However, the portion of the current that flows through R1 is

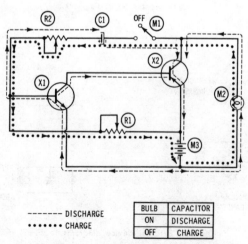

BULB	CAPACITOR
ON	DISCHARGE
OFF	CHARGE

- - - - - - - DISCHARGE
• • • • • • CHARGE

Fig. 4-5A. Stroboscope current-flow paths.

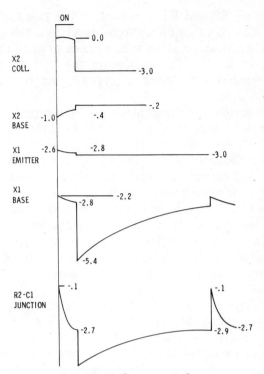

Fig. 4-5B. Stroboscope waveforms.

critical because it is the bias current for X1. As R1 is increased
the bias current is decreased, eventually reaching a point where
X1 is no longer forward biased, and thereupon stops conducting. When this happens, X2 is turned off and the lamp goes out.

A considerably different situation exists, however, when the
feedback network is connected. A charge and discharge path
for the feedback capacitors must now be fitted into the picture.

Using the time when lamp M2 is glowing as a reference, the
complete cycle can be divided into two parts (Fig. 4-5B) :

Lamp on—discharge,
Lamp off—charge

The charge path for C1 is from the negative terminal of M3,
through the lamp (the current is too low to cause the filament
to glow), and into the negative terminal of C1. To complete
the electron path, electrons travel from the positive terminal

of C1, through R2 and R1, and back to the positive terminal of battery M3. This flow of electrons develops a voltage on the base of X1 which is negative with respect to the emitter, and X1 is reverse biased. The voltage on the base of X2 is not sufficiently negative to forward bias X2, and the lamp does not light.

After a period of time, however, the capacitor charge reaches a point where the X1 base voltage is positive with respect to the emitter. Electron flow through the C1-R2-R1 path diminishes sufficiently, due to the increasing resistance of C1 as it nears full charge, to cause the voltage across R1 to become smaller, or nearer zero, and the electron flow from emitter to base in X1 results in the emitter being negative with respect to the base. X1 then goes into conduction.

When X1 goes into conduction, so does X2, and the lamp glows brightly for the length of time it takes for C1 to discharge through X2, M3 (+ to −), X1 (base to emitter), R2, and the positive terminal of C1.

The discharge of C1 does not directly light lamp M2. The lamp lights because the collector-emitter resistance in series with the lamp and the battery is very low when X2 conducts. The length of time that lamp M2 is on, however, is controlled by C1, (and R2), because as C1 discharges, the positive voltage on the base of X1 approaches zero, X1 is no longer forward biased and stops conducting. X2 is then turned off and the lamp goes out, completing the cycle.

CHAPTER 5

A Magic Lamp

While the device to be described is not really "magic," it will serve, for example, as a completely self-contained, automatic, cordless night lamp. The handy little self-switching light is shown in Fig. 5-1. It demonstrates another application

Fig. 5-1. The "magic" lamp.

of the photocell. This circuit[1] utilizes a photovoltaic (voltage generating) cell as an input signal source of a complementary symmetry amplifier similar to those often used in computers as indicator or relay drivers.

[1] Courtesy International Rectifier Corp.

Aside from the novelty value of a light that turns itself on at night and off with the coming of day, this lamp can serve as a very-low-candlepower night light. It will enable you to distinguish large objects in the middle of the night. (Who knows, it may even prevent a sore toe sometime.)

CONSTRUCTION

Most of the layout details are indicated in Figs 5-1 and 5-2. The circuit diagram is shown in Fig. 5-3.

Note the method of mounting photocell PC1. It is insulated from the chassis box by the plastic screws which hold it in position (Fig. 5-4). As the nuts are tightened, the screws exert a side pressure on the cell; this makes a very firm mounting. Small holes near the rear edge of the box permit passing the leads from the cell to the terminal strip inside. While certainly not the only method of mounting this type of cell, the technique does offer considerable advantage in economy.

There are several types of selenium photocells; the type shown in Fig. 5-1 is about the least expensive because the manufacturer didn't have to put any time or money into a mounting. Other types of cells (e.g., plug-in, etc.), while simplifying the mounting problem, add greatly to the expense of the project. In this respect, a little bargain hunting might be to your advantage. If you seek a substitute for the cell shown in the parts list, be certain that you get one with the following characteristics:

At an illumination of 100 footcandles, and a load resistance of 100 ohms, a current of 700 or more microamperes shall flow. A cell with less output may cause improper operation of the magic lamp.

Since the life of the No. 49 pilot light is indefinite in length for this application, it should be soldered into the circuit, as shown in Fig. 5-2. The 1½-volt battery life is more than four weeks; it can also be soldered into the circuit. The clip (not shown) for holding this battery inside the box is mounted on the bottom half of the chassis box. The leads visible on the right side of Fig. 5-2 are used to make the connections to the battery.

48

Parts List

Item	Description
R1	47K, ½-watt resistor
X1	2N535 or 2N591 PNP transistor (preferably the former)
X2	2N214 NPN transistor
M1	No. 49 pilot lamp
M2	1.5-volt cell (Burgess 210, Eveready 1050, RCA VS036, or equivalent)
PC1	International Rectifier Corp. A15 selenium photocell, or equivalent
Misc.	2¼ × 2¼ × 4-inch aluminum box (Bud CU-2103-A or equivalent), rubber grommet, 5-lug terminal strip, plastic screws, machine screws, nuts, and wire.

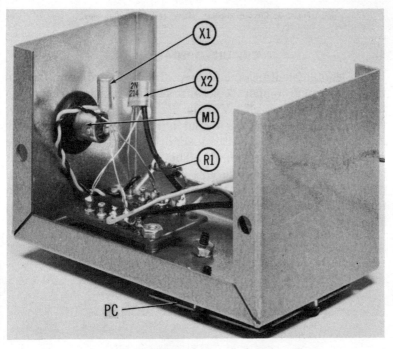

Fig. 5-2. Internal view of chassis.

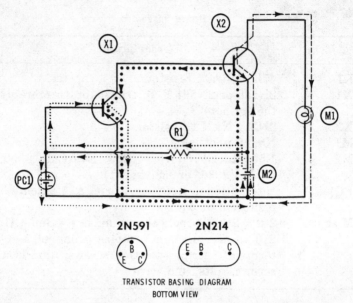

2N591

2N214

TRANSISTOR BASING DIAGRAM
BOTTOM VIEW

Fig. 5-3. Circuit, current paths, and base diagrams.

CIRCUIT OPERATION

The complementary-symmetry, direct-coupled amplifier is very economical to operate because neither transistor conducts when the circuit is off. With no light shining on the photo-voltaic cell (Fig. 5-3), its output is virtually zero. Transistor X1 is forward biased with a slightly negative base voltage from the battery through R1. The X1 collector voltage, and hence the X2 base voltage, are each about −1.0 volt. This is positive with respect to the X2 emitter so that X2 is also forward biased and conducts through its collector load, lamp M1. The paths of electron flow are as follows: From the nega-

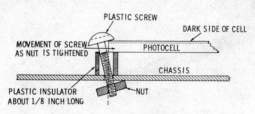

Fig. 5-4. Photocell mounting details.

tive terminal of battery M2, through R1 and the base-emitter circuit of X1 and back to the positive terminal of M2. A parallel path is through the emitter-base circuit of X2, through the X1 collector-emitter circuit to M2. A third parallel path is through the X2 emitter-collector circuit, through M1 to the positive battery terminal; this one lights the lamp.

When light impinges on PC1, a voltage is generated which is of opposite polarity to the X1 forward bias voltage and is great enough to reverse bias X1. The X1 collector voltage rises toward the battery voltage and acts to reverse bias X2 so that no current flows in the X2-collector-M1 circuit and the lamp goes out.

Since the current that flows when light is striking the photocell (X1 and X2 both off) is very low (not more than 200 microamperes) and since the circuit is off when the ambient light exceeds about 1 footcandle, it can be seen that the battery which powers the circuit could last well in excess of a month.

CHAPTER 6

Analog Addition

In an analog computer, addition is performed in a manner wholly different from that used in a digital computer. Analog computers do not generally deal in fixed amounts, where a quantity is represented by an arbitrary symbol, such as the number 2. Rather they operate with variable quantities that are used to represent something else; with continuous values, not values that jump from step to step. Consequently their answers are in the same form, i.e., continuously varying indications that are analogous to a continuously occurring mechanical or electrical function.

To accomplish this sort of computation in a digital computer would necessitate its being able to handle infinitely long numbers. Why? Because the next voltage above 1.000 . . . 0∞ volt, for example, is 1.0 plus an infinitesimal fraction of a volt. This small number can only be written as a very long string of zeros to the right of the decimal point, followed by a significant digit. The smaller the capacity of the machine, the less precision it is capable of achieving.

However, within the limits imposed by its construction, a digital computer can give exact answers, as in a payroll accounting problem, or stock inventory calculation. An analog computer can never attain this sort of accuracy, for all its quantities are approximations, analogs of physical quantities whose exact measurement is virtually impossible. Even so, the analog computer is capable of accuracy measured in tenths, hundredths, or even thousandths of a per cent. Also, an analog computer will operate on problems that simply are not feasible on digital computers; can you imagine a digital computer declaring, at the end of a payroll computation "Pay John Doe *about* $100." Such a declaration would give a CPA apoplexy.

Yet this is the equivalent of what analog computers often do. You may well ask "Why would anyone want a machine that can't give exact answers?" The answer is that an analog computer can't give answers any more accurate than the question—there are many mechanical phenomena which engineering science does not understand well enough even to phrase questions that will enable the computer to produce the desired answer. The analog computer is valuable because it can "come close"; its answers, while not perfect, are "good enough." Good enough, that is, to give the engineer a place to start, and between the man and the machine, perfection *can* be approached. The analog computer is definitely a very *practical* machine.

ABOUT THE CIRCUIT

The circuit used in the analog adder utilizes two resistances in series to limit the flow of current through a milliammeter. This current indication is calibrated in terms of the numbers shown on the dial of M3, and the totals can therefore be read from this meter.

Construction

The analog adder is constructed on a square piece of 1/8-inch Masonite, eight inches on a side. The hole for the meter is cut first; this can be done quite simply by drilling a lot of tiny holes close together in a circle slightly smaller than the meter. Then punch out the panel inside these holes and file the resulting hole to the proper size and smoothness.

Next, lay out the locations for the verniers, the push-button switch, and the calibration potentiometer, and mount these components as shown in Figs. 6-1 and 6-2. The strap used to hold potentiometers R2 and R3 is made from a piece of the material called "chimney strap," which is used by TV technicians in mounting antennas and lead-in cables.

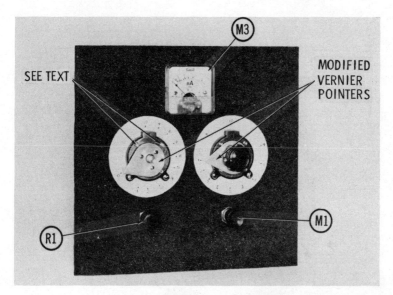

SEE TEXT

M3

MODIFIED
VERNIER
POINTERS

R1

M1

Fig. 6-1. Front panel of analog adder.

Battery M2 is soldered directly to one terminal of switch M1 in order to simplify the wiring as much as possible. If you wish to mount M2 separately, this can be done simply by using a small piece of the "chimney strap" formed into a suitable bracket and held under one of the screws used to mount the verniers.

The verniers give an ease and smoothness of adjustment to the potentiometers that could not be obtained in any other way. However, some vernier modification will be necessary to get the proper amount of rotation indication. This modification consists of two steps; removing the old dials and putting on new pointers, and removing the vernier rotation stops.

The first step is shown in Fig. 6-1, where the knob has been removed to show the shape and mounting style of the new pointer. The second step is to remove the vernier from its plastic case by taking out the four tiny screws pointed out in Fig. 6-1. File off the little square ear that projects from the periphery of the largest brass wheel. Do *not* try to eliminate the stops by breaking off or filing smooth the plastic projection against which the square ear or lug strikes—the plastic case can be broken quite easily.

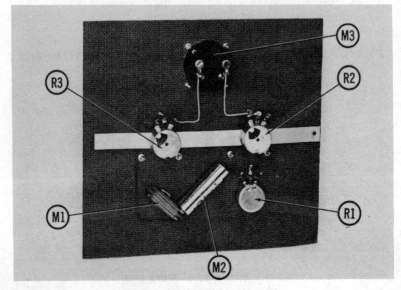

Fig. 6-2. Rear view of analog adder.

When this task has been completed and the vernier re-assembled, cut two circles of plain white paper two inches in diameter and place them under the verniers before remounting the latter. The holes cut in the paper (for the mounting screws) should be very carefully located so they do not show when mounted.

The next step is to wire the adder according to Fig. 6-3. The circuit should be wired just as shown (Fig. 6-2) so the dials will indicate properly. Be careful when wiring the potentiom-

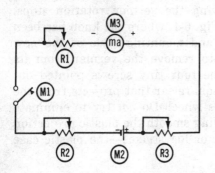

Fig. 6-3. Circuit diagram of adder.

eters lest melted solder flux run into the resistance element and ruin the potentiometer.

Parts List

Item	Description
R1	2.5K, ½-watt carbon potentiometer
R2, R3	10K, 1-watt, linear resistance, carbon potentiometer
M1	switch, SPST n/o momentary contact
M2	1½-volt battery
M3	0-1 ma meter
Vernier	vernier dial (Calrad VD-36, or equivalent)
Misc.	Push-button for switch M1, (1) ; pointer for vernier, modified as per text (2) ; Masonite panel, ⅛-inch thick, eight inches square, (1).

Calibration

Calibration can best be accomplished by using an ohmmeter to measure the full scale resistance of the potentiometers and marking each dial (the circles of blank white paper made in an earlier step) with a 10. Then lower the resistance 1,000 ohms and mark the dial with a 9, and so on down to 1,000 ohms, and a 1. Do the same with both R2 and R3.

Then set either R2 or R3 on *1*, and place a mark on the piece of white paper pasted over the meter face (Fig. 6-1). Then move the other potentiometer to *1* (leave the first one set at *1*) and mark 2 on the meter scale. Continue by setting the first potentiometer to *2*, then when M1 is depressed, write a 3 on the meter scale; 2 plus 1 equals 3. Then set the second potentiometer to *2*, depress M1 and write a 4 over the meter indication; 2 plus 2 equals 4. This process should be continued as long as you can discern between positions of the meter needle. Another simpler, but somewhat less accurate, way to calibrate the potentiometers is merely to divide the rotation into 10 even parts, each of which should be (and usually is) fairly close to 1,000 ohms.

R1 is provided to set the meter to full-scale indication when both verniers are set at zero, and M1 is closed.

To use the adder, you merely set one number on each of the two potentiometers, depress M1, and read the total on the meter. A similar application would be to set one dial to a known value, the other to a random setting, then depress M1; by subtracting the known value from the meter reading, the value of the other setting could be determined.

CHAPTER 7

Electronic Tachometer

Electronic tachometers, or revolution counters, as they are sometimes called, can serve several useful functions in connection with your automobile engine. They can be used to indicate either gear-shift points, or the point at which your engine is achieving maximum torque. Using a tachometer in conjunction with the information presented in the owner's manual for your car regarding maximum power, torque, etc., and their relationship to engine rpm, your car can be driven either for maximum fuel economy, or for maximum horsepower. The tachometer will tell you when you have reached the point indicated in your owner's manual, and help you keep your rpm at that rate.

If you will make a chart of speed versus rpm for each gear, the tachometer can serve as an emergency speedometer, even on automobiles with automatic transmissions.

ABOUT THE CIRCUIT

The basic part of the circuit used in the electronic tachometer is known as a Schmitt trigger. Schematically it is similar in appearance to several other types of flip-flop or multivibrator circuits, but its operation is considerably different. Like any flip-flop, the Schmitt trigger has two possible states, either on or off. However, instead of changing its state for a definite length of time when pulsed (as does a monostable vibrator) or changing its state and remaining in the new state when pulsed (as does a flip-flop), the Schmitt trigger will change its state when pulsed for the duration of the pulse only.

A very common application of this action in computers is in connection with circuit breakers, switches, and relay contacts. Normally, when circuit breaker contacts close, the leading edge of the pulse generated is very ragged due to contact bounce (Fig. 7-1A), and if applied to a sensitive electronic circuit, can cause decidedly improper operation. To prevent this, an integrating circuit is used between the circuit-breaker contact and the input to the Schmitt trigger. When the input

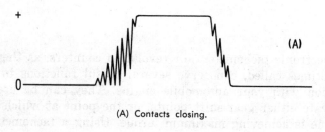

(A) Contacts closing.

(B) Pulse with integrating circuit between contacts and trigger.

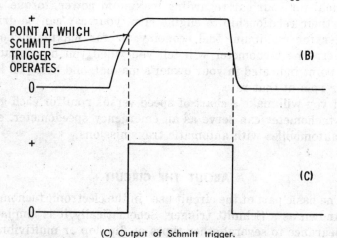

(C) Output of Schmitt trigger.

Fig. 7-1. Waveforms produced by the closing of circuit-breaker contacts.

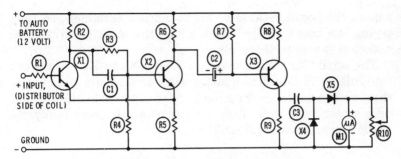

Fig. 7-2. Circuit of electronic tachometer.

reaches a critical value (Fig. 7-1B), the trigger will "flip" almost instantaneously, and will remain in the new condition as long as the circuit-breaker contacts are closed (Fig. 7-1C). A similar action occurs when the contacts open. The fast rise time of the trigger output pulse is adequate for use in electronic circuits where the pulses in Figs. 7-1A and B would not be.

If a 6.3-volts AC input signal is fed to the circuit shown in Fig. 7-2, and the power leads are connected to a voltage source (12 volts DC), the output at the junction of C2 and R6 will be a 60-cps square wave such as that shown in Fig. 7-1C, with a leading-edge rise time of about one microsecond.

CONSTRUCTION

The electronic tachometer was built in two styles for automobiles with the negative-ground electrical systems (Fig. 7-2) found in most American models.

Fig. 7-3 shows a method of constructing the electronic portion of the tachometer so that it occupies a space scarcely larger than the meter itself. The circuit is built using a phenolic circuit board that was trimmed to the shape shown with a pair of tin snips.

The method shown in Fig. 7-3 for mounting some of the resistors (e.g., R3) was adopted because of the tight space limitations imposed by the small working area. However, the finished product can be installed in the dashboard of an automobile with little concern for fitting problems.

Fig. 7-4 shows the parts arrangement on the side of the board next to the meter. There won't be much room on this side of the board because of the two meter terminals, so keep trying the board on the terminals as the work progresses to make certain everything fits.

The small "flea" clips visible in Figs. 7-3 and 7-4 are a great convenience in this close-quarter work as they slip quite easily through the holes in the circuit board, yet hold tightly and take solder very well. They can be obtained from Lafayette Radio Corp. (Stock #MS263).

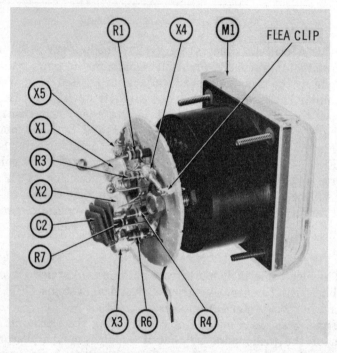

Fig. 7-3. Electronic portion of tachometer.

Capacitors C2 and C3 are made up of .1-mfd ceramic disc capacitors wired in parallel. C2 and C3 are each made up of three of these capacitors, although only two are shown in C3. The third was added after the photograph was made, so that the two capacitors, C2 and C3, are just alike. C2 and C3 can each be replaced by a single .33-mfd, 15-volt paper capacitor.

If you wish to avoid the cramped quarters occasioned by the type of construction shown in Figs. 7-3 and 7-4, you can build the unit as shown in Figs. 7-5 and 7-6. If this type of construction is used, the electronic section can be located wherever convenient, and wires can be used to carry the impulses to the meter. Note that there are some differences in parts; C2, for example, is two 1.0-mfd electrolytic capacitors (6 volts DC) in series to make 0.5-mfd capacitor. C3 (Fig. 7-6) is a different type of capacitor; however, the circuit is essentially the same as that shown in the previous illustrations.

The tachometer can be used on cars with a positive ground system if the following changes are made:

1. X1 and X2 should be 2N396 PNP transistors.
2. X3 should be a 2N414 PNP transistor.
3. X4 and X5 should be reversed.

Fig. 7-4. Circuit board for mounting on the rear of meter.

4. M1 connections should be reversed.
5. The polarity of the connections shown in Fig. 7-2 should be reversed to make the schematic read correctly.

CALIBRATION

Calibration of the electronic tachometer can be accomplished in several ways:

1. Connect it into a car which already has a tachometer, and mark the dial at appropriate points according to the other tachometer indication. If you use this method, be sure the other car has the same number of cylinders, and a 12-volt ignition system.
2. A calibrated oscilloscope can be used to measure the distance between pulses and the number of rpm can be calculated according to the following:
   a. 8-cylinder, 4-cycle engine—rpm equals 15 times the number of pulses (spark) per second.
   b. 6-cylinder, 4-cycle engine—rpm equals 20 times the number of pulses per second.
   c. 4-cylinder, 4-cycle engine—rpm equals 30 times the number of spark pulses per second.

The number of pulses per second is calculated by dividing the time between the leading edge of the pulses (in seconds) into 1.0. For example, in an 8-cylinder, 4-cycle

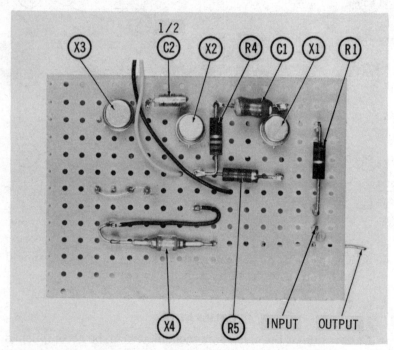

Fig. 7-5. Alternate method of circuit board construction.

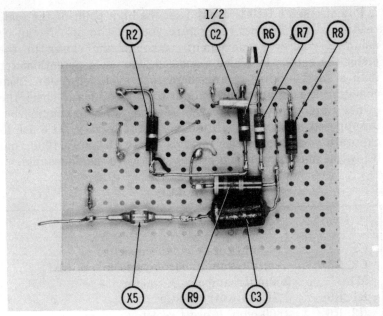

Fig. 7-6. Another view of alternate configuration.

engine, pulses .005 second (5 msec) apart, divided into 1.0 equals 200 pulses per second. This figure times 15 equals 3000 rpm.

3. An ordinary oscilloscope can be used to measure the distance between pulses. This distance should be marked on the scope screen. Then use an audio voltage generator to make a sine wave signal one cycle of which just exactly fills the distance between the marks you have made on the scope screen. The number of pulses per minute can then be read directly from the signal generator dial and the rpm calculation made as described earlier.

If an audio signal generator is not available, a 6.3-volts AC, 60-cps signal can be used. One cycle of this frequency occurs in about 17 milliseconds (.0166 seconds). So a half cycle would measure about 8.5 milliseconds, and a quarter cycle about 4¼ milliseconds. These times can be used to estimate the time between pulses coming from the automobile circuit-breaker points. Once this time is established, the frequency can be calculated and hence the rpm.

Potentiometer R10 is used to set the high point of the scale reading at the highest rpm figure you wish to use. It can be mounted wherever convenient, although the closer to the meter the better. It is also a good idea to use a potentiometer with a shaft-locking arrangement to prevent vibration from changing the calibration. It might be a good idea to check the owner's manual for your car to see what the maximum rpm is supposed to be, although there is actually very little use to calibrate your tachometer for this figure. A figure 1000 rpm below the maximum would probably be more than adequate.

Parts List

Item	Description
C1	220-mmf ceramic disc capacitor
C2, C3	.3-mfd ceramic disc capacitor (see text)
M1	200-microampere DC meter
R1, R9	4.7K, ½-watt resistor
R2, R6	1800-ohm, ½-watt resistor
R3	18K, ½-watt resistor
R4	15K, ½-watt resistor
R5	560-ohm, ½-watt resistor
R7	150K, ½-watt resistor
R8	150-ohm, ½-watt resistor
R10	2.5K carbon potentiometer
X1, X2, X3	2N585 NPN transistor
X4, X5	1N120 germanium diode
Misc.	perforated circuit board; flea clips (see text); solder lugs to fit over meter terminals.

CIRCUIT OPERATION

The electronic tachometer is a combination of two basic computer circuits—the Schmitt trigger and the emitter follower.

The Schmitt trigger is a regenerative bistable circuit, the condition of which is determined by the magnitude of the input voltage. For example, in Fig. 7-2, with input signal voltage such that X1 is not conducting, current flow through the voltage divider R2, R3, and R4 causes about 5 volts bias to appear at the base of X2. The emitters of X1 and X2 are at about 4.8 volts because of the forward bias voltage requirements of X2 (about .2 volts). Therefore, if the input voltage is less than 4.8 volts, X1 will not conduct (as was assumed earlier).

However, as the voltage on the base of X1 is increased toward 4.8 volts, a point is reached at which X1 begins to conduct, and its collector voltage drops toward zero. This negative voltage shift appears at the base of X2, reverse biasing this transistor, and causing it to stop conducting.

The speed with which this process takes place is greatly increased by the use of a small capacitor (C1) across R3. This capacitor is called a commutative capacitor (commutate means to lead or direct), and due to its presence in this circuit any voltage shift appearing on the collector of X1 will be immediately sensed at the base of X2. This happens because as X1 collector voltage drops, C1 discharges through the R4, R5 and X1 emitter-to-collector circuit such that the base of X2 is negative with respect to its emitter; hence it is cut off.

The Schmitt trigger will remain in this condition as long as the input signal amplitude exceeds the critical triggering voltage (about 4.8 volts). If this signal falls below another critical voltage, X1 is cut off, the voltage at its emitter rises as does the X2 base voltage, and X2 begins conducting.

The stage containing X3 is a form of emitter follower—after the flip-flop one of the most common circuits in the modern electronic computer. Emitter followers are used primarily because of their high input impedance (and consequent light circuit loading) and low output impedance.

The emitter follower circuit in Fig. 7-2 is composed of R7, R8, R9, and X3; it has been modified from the basic emitter follower circuit for purposes of bias stabilization and reduction of input impedance variations. R7 has been added to form a divider network with the base-emitter junction and R9. Since its value is so large, fluctuation in bias, either because of leakage current through R9 or load-current variations, will be minimized. C2 serves to keep the differing voltages on the collector of X2 and the base of X3 from interfering with each other, since there is several' volts difference between these points under static conditions.

R8 serves to greatly reduce, or eliminate, changes in input impedance due to changes in load current. Without this resistor, variations in load resistance will cause a change in the voltage developed across the load resistor, therefore varying the input impedance of X3. The signal-opposing voltage drop across R8 (or the drop in voltage at the collector), times the current gain of X3, is effectively placed in series with the signal, so that it acts to buck any change in input impedance.

C3 couples the square wave output of the emitter follower to the diodes X4 and X5 in the form of positive-going pulses. X4 filters to ground (−12 volts) any negative going spikes on the signal. X5 directs the positive pulses to the meter which gives an average voltage reading. When the engine speed is increased the pulse repetition rate is increased and the meter, which acts to integrate the sharp pulses, indicates a higher average voltage. Potentiometer R10 is for calibration of the meter.

CHAPTER 8

Counting With Relays

If a computer is to have any value, one of the things it must be able to do is count. You might not recognize the method that a computer uses in counting. Perhaps you've noticed whenever a person "ticks off" several points during a discussion he is likely to use his fingers to count them—the first finger being point one, the second finger being point two, the third finger point three, and so forth. Using such a system, he will be limited to a maximum of ten points, unless he starts over (or happens to be barefoot).

Consider the possibilities if the man were to count like a computer does. How high could the total be? Well, of course, a computer doesn't count the same way as a human; using the same example as above, the computer would count *its* arguments as shown in Fig. 8-1, using binary flip-flops as tallies instead of fingers. (Binary means two-valued, i.e., on-off, open-closed, etc.; these two values are represented by the digits 0 and 1.) The first pulse would turn on FF1, and the 1 lamp would glow. The second pulse would turn off FF1 and turn on FF2, and the 2 lamp would be lit. The third pulse would turn on FF1 again—FF2 does not go off (in a binary counter, a flip-flop changes its state only when the one preceding it or the pulse that feeds it is turned *off*), so both the 1 and 2 lamps would glow, indicating a total of three pulses counted. Yet only two counting flip-flops (the fingers and toes of the machine) have been used. If another pulse is counted, both the 1

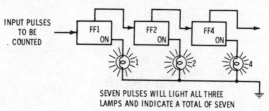

SEVEN PULSES WILL LIGHT ALL THREE
LAMPS AND INDICATE A TOTAL OF SEVEN

Fig. 8-1. Basic flip-flop counting system.

and the 2 flip-flops will be turned off, and the 4 flip-flop (and lamp) will be turned on. Using these three elements, the count can go as high as seven. How? Table 8-1 shows just how this is done.

Table 8-1. Counting to seven with three flip-flops.

Impulse	Lamps On
0	none
1	1
2	2
3	1, 2
4	4
5	4, 1
6	4, 2
7	4, 2, 1

The use of such a three-element counting method requires some work on the part of the person reading the three indicator lamps, because the information is in a type of arrangement known as "octal coding." This form of coding gets its name from the fact that there are eight possible combinations, ranging from zero to seven. Octal coding is a form of shorthand for binary notation, and is utilized chiefly by computer programmers and maintenance personnel as a convenience in writing long binary numbers in a more easily used form. Table 8-2 shows that the binary number 001010011100 is equal in value to the octal number 1234; obviously the latter is considerably more convenient. Octal 1234 equals 668 in everyday decimal. Binary and octal are like decimal in that the units position is on the right.

If, at this point, one more flip-flop is added, the count is no longer limited to seven, but can go as high as 15, although

Table 8-2. Binary to octal conversion.

Flip-Flops	4 2 1	4 2 1	4 2 1	4 2 1
Binary	0 0 1	0 1 0	0 1 1	1 0 0
Octal	1	2	3	4

usually the count is stopped at 9. In this way a decimal (0 through 9) counter has been made using only binary elements. These counters can be read directly by adding the value of the glowing lamps as in the example in Fig. 8-2. Note that several positions (10 through 15) have been wasted—even so, this method of counting (known as binary coded demical, or BCD) is more economical of components than assigning a value of one to each flip-flop—or finger or toe! This method can be carried out quite a bit further than four positions. Indeed, to answer the question posed earlier, if a man using *ten* fingers counted like a computer does, he could total as high as 1,023.

CONSTRUCTION

Flip-flops are not the only way to make a counter for use in a computer. Another form of binary device is the relay—it is either energized or de-energized! Fig. 8-3 shows a relay counter which can count to nine, and which demonstrates the principle of binary coded decimal indication using the neon lamps on the right end of the counter. The use of relays in counting circuits is quite common. Indeed, some electromechanical computers use nothing but relays and cams in their entire operation.

Figs. 8-4 and 8-5 show the construction details of the relay counter. The input pulses are obtained by using a 4PDT switch

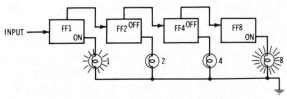

Fig. 8-2. A BCD counter showing total of nine.

(*I* in Fig. 8-5) which should be of the type that remains latched when the button is depressed, and returns to normal when the button is again depressed. If you can't find a 4PDT latching push-button switch, a 4PDT relay operated by a SPST latching switch may be substituted (Fig. 8-6).

The unit shown in Fig. 8-3 was constructed in an 8 × 6 × 3½-inch aluminum box. However, it is suggested that you get the relays first, before buying any type of container. While the relays used in the original counter operate from 115 volts AC,

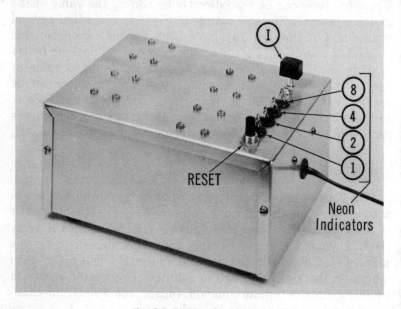

Fig. 8-3. Binary relay counter.

you may find other types of relays more plentiful or economical. One possible source of 4PDT relays (with 6-volt DC coils) at reasonable prices is C and H Sales Company, 2176 East Colorado Blvd., Pasadena 8, California. In any event, be sure of the size of the relays you are going to use before getting a container for the completed device. If you use a different type of relay, the neon-resistor combination which is used with the 110-volt AC coils shown in Figs. 8-4 and 8-5 may not operate satisfactorily. In this case use filament-type bulbs of the proper voltage. The best way of wiring the resistor-neon indicators is

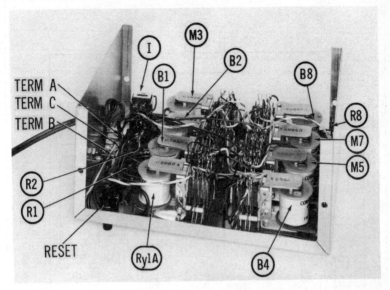

Fig. 8-4. Internal construction of relay counter.

to solder the 100K resistor to one relay coil terminal; then add a wire to the other end of the resistor and one to the other relay coil terminal, and run them both to where the neon is protruding through the grommet.

If you intend to experiment further with this circuit (and this is strongly recommended both for fun and knowledge), you may find that a more suitable method of mounting the eight (or nine) relays is to fasten them to a piece of wood or metal angle stock such that the relays are side by side in a straight line. This greatly simplifies construction, tracing wiring, and making changes.

Note that some of the relays (B2, for example) are energized through their own normally closed contacts. This means that as the relay is energized, this contact will open and remove the energization voltage. However, due to momentum, the armature should continue to move enough to permit the holding contact (B2-1, normally open, in this example) to close and thus keep the relay energized. If, due to the type of relay armature, contact adjustment, etc., the armature travel (after the normally closed contact opens) is not sufficient to close the nor-

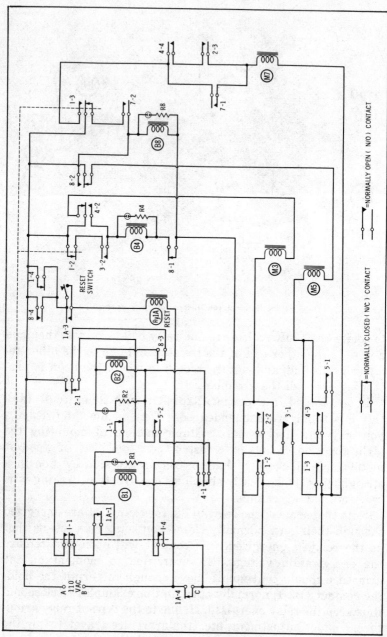

Fig. 8-5. Circuit diagram of counter.

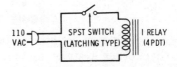

Fig. 8-6. Use of a relay in place of switch I.

mally open point, the relay armature will drop back to normal. If this happens the relay will buzz loudly as it continuously picks up and drops back to normal. Perhaps it will eventually stay energized and perhaps not. In any event, the cure is either to adjust the normally closed contact closer to the transfer contact (be sure the normally closed and normally open contacts do not touch the transfer contact at the same time), or to use a different type of relay. Perhaps the best idea is to test the relay for this type of operation before using it in the counter. This can be done very simply by temporarily wiring the relay as shown in Fig. 8-7 and applying power. The relay

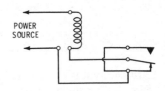

Fig. 8-7. Test for relay energization characteristics.

should pick up with a sharp click. If it doesn't, check for binds in the armature, or try the adjustment mentioned earlier.

Parts List

Item	Description
R1, R2, R4, R8	100K, ½-watt resistor
I	4PDT push-to-close/push-to-open switch
Indicator lamps	NE-2 neon lamps
Relays	115-volts AC, 4PDT (Comar type R, see text)
Reset switch	SPST n/o, momentary contact
Misc.	Aluminum box, rubber grommets to fit ⅜-inch hole (5), rubber feet (4), power cord and plug.

Although this counter is based on the BCD idea discussed earlier, other systems are possible; indeed, even widely used. You will find that wiring a counter to operate using either of the two forms shown in Tables 8-3 and 8-4 would prove to be a fascinating and challenging task.

Table 8-3. Biquinary system.

	4	3	2	1	0	5	0
0	0	0	0	0	1	0	1
1	0	0	0	1	0	0	1
2	0	0	1	0	0	0	1
3	0	1	0	0	0	0	1
4	1	0	0	0	0	0	1
5	0	0	0	0	1	1	0
6	0	0	0	1	0	1	0
7	0	0	1	0	0	1	0
8	0	1	0	0	0	1	0
9	1	0	0	0	0	1	0

Using a system of neon indicators like those in the counter of Fig. 8-5, the two systems shown in Tables 8-3 and 8-4 would have the neons lit only where a 1 is shown in the squares. (More than four neons will be needed, of course, in these systems.) For example, note that in the biquinary system, a neon across the 0 (zero) relay coil would be lit for half the numbers, as would a neon across the coil of the 5 relay.

Table 8-4. Two out of five system.

0	1	1	0	0	0
1	0	0	0	1	1
2	0	0	1	0	1
3	0	0	1	1	0
4	0	1	0	0	1
5	0	1	0	1	0
6	0	1	1	0	0
7	1	0	0	0	1
8	1	0	0	1	0
9	1	0	1	0	0

CIRCUIT OPERATION

The following discussion should be used in conjunction with the circuit diagram shown in Fig. 8-5 as an aid in trouble-shooting the counter, in understanding some of the principles of relay circuitry, and as a guide if you wish to experiment further with other types of relay counting circuits.

Ry1A

Ry1A is used as a reset relay. It can be energized (picked up) only when switch I is in the normal position or relay B8 is energized. Opening the Ry1A-4 n/c contact will de-energize every relay in the counter except B1. Ry1A is also used as an *initial* reset, because if *I* is normal when power is supplied to the counter, relay B2 will pick up through the following circuit: from terminal A, through I-1 n/c, Ry1A-1 n/c, B1-1 n/c, B2-1 n/c, B8-3 n/c, through the B2 relay coil, then through B4-1 n/c to terminal C. Once energized, B2 can hold itself up through the B2-1 n/c contact.

Opening the Ry1A-1 n/c and the Ry1A-4 n/c contacts will de-energize (drop out) B2 and prevent a holding circuit for that relay as long as Ry1A-4 n/c is open. Ry1A holding circuit is as follows; from terminal A through B1-4 n/c, Ry1A-3 n/o (now closed since Ry1A has been energized), the relay coil and thence to terminal B. Ry1A will remain transferred from the time the reset button is pushed until B1 is energized.

Switch I

This 4PDT latching switch is used primarily to pick and hold B1 (through I-1 n/c). Other I contacts condition various relay energization circuits; e.g., I-4 n/o is used to prevent the count from jumping from three to six, by opening the B2 pick-and-hold circuits used when B4 is energized. (When B4 is energized, and B1 is normal, B2 *could* pick through the B4-1 n/o contact *except for I-4 n/o!*)

B1

B1 is the binary-one relay—it is energized directly from 110 volts AC through I-1 n/o and is held through that contact as long as *I* is transferred. This relay is energized for each odd number.

B2

B2 is the binary-two relay; when it is energized it indicates that at least two impulses have occurred. It is energized as follows: from terminal A through I-1 n/c, through Ry1A-1 n/c, B1-1 n/c, B2-1 n/c, B8-3 n/c, B4-1 n/c to terminal C. B2 holds through its B2-1 n/o contact.

M3

The M3 relay is used as a memory device. It remembers that since relays B1 and B2 have been energized at the same time, the next step is to energize B4. M3 is picked up as follows: from terminal C through B1-2 n/o, B2-2 n/o, M3 coil, then through B4-2 n/c to terminal A. It is held transferred through M3-1 n/o, M3 coil, and B4-2 until relay B4 is energized. M3 is necessary to insure an energization circuit for B4 during the short interval after B1 has been de-energized (due to the I-1 n/o contact opening) and before the I-2 n/c contact closes. Although this interval is very short, it is the reason why B1 and B2 contacts can not be used to energize B4; i.e., B1 and B2 would *both* have to remain energized (to show that a three count had taken place) until the I-4 n/c contact had closed, in order to pick up B4. Yet this could never happen because B1 is held up through a normally open I contact, and it will open (and drop B1) before any of the normally closed I contacts close.

B4

B4 is the binary-four relay. When energized it indicates that four impulses have occurred. It is energized as follows: I-2 n/c, M3-2 n/o, relay coil, B8-1 n/c, to terminal C. B4 is held up through B4-2 n/o (closed when B4 is energized).

The B4-1 n/c contact opens the holding circuit for relay B2, and B1 is dropped out when I-1 n/o returns to normal. M3 is de-energized when B4-2 n/c is opened; hence, at the end of four counts only B4 is energized.

M5

Relay M5 is used to remember that five counts have occurred, and that on the next impulse the count must go to six. M5 is necessary in energizing B2 because the normal energizing path, using B4-1 n/c, is no longer available since B4 is energized. M5-2 now furnishes a path through which relay B2 can be picked up to show, in conjunction with relay B4, a total of six counts.

M5 is picked up as follows: from terminal A, through B8-2 n/c, M5 relay coil, B4-3 n/o, B1-2 n/o, to terminal C. This relay is held up through M5-1 n/o.

M7

Relay M7 also serves as a memory relay. It remembers that seven impulses have occurred, and the count must go to eight after the next impulse. Lest you think that, instead of M7-2 n/o, B1, B2, and B4 all energized at once (in conjunction with switch I) would suffice to pick relay B8, remember that before

Table 8-5. Status of relays after each impulse.

Pulse	Relay Conditions
Reset	Ry1A energized
1	B1 energized
2	B2 energized
3	B1, B2, M3 energized
4	B4 energized
5	B1, B4, M5 energized
6	B2, B4, M5 energized
7	B1, B2, B4, M5, M7 energized
8	M7, B8 energized
9	B1, M7, B8 energized
Reset	Ry1A energized

I-3 n/c makes contact, I-1 would have dropped B1 and opened this B8 energization circuit before B8 ever had a chance to pick up! This gap—between I-1 n/o opening, and I-3 n/c closing—is the reason why B1, B2, and B4 contacts are not used to pick B8, but M7 is.

M7 is energized when I-3 n/o closes (indicating an odd count) after B2-3 n/o and B4-4 n/o have closed (indicating at least six impulses have occurred), the circuit from terminal A to terminal C being completed when these contacts close. M7 holds through M7-1 n/o.

B8 is the binary-eight relay; it becomes energized when eight impulses have occurred. It is energized through I-3 n/c and M7-2 n/o. B8-1 is used to drop B4. B8-2 serves two purposes; B8-2 n/c is used in the hold circuit of M5, and B8-2 n/o is used to hold B8. B8-3 n/c is used to drop out B2 when going from seven to eight. B8-4 is used to permit a reset after the ninth impulse has been counted.

The conditions of the relays after each impulse are shown in Table 8-5.

CHAPTER 9

Logic Lock

How would you like to have a lock with a combination that couldn't be found accidentally. (Well, perhaps it *could* be found, but the odds against it happening are so great they are almost unbelievable.) Such a device is the logic lock. Using the four switches shown in Fig. 9-1, the likelihood of selecting the correct combination, for any given trial, is 1 in 25,937,424,601. Or, to put it another way, each time you take a guess at the combination, you have a 0.000000003 chance of finding it. Wouldn't you agree that such a lock would be mighty hard to pick?

Yet the combination can be very easy to remember since it's divided into three groups—each of which could be chosen to have special meaning for you so that you would not forget.

The logic lock could be useful in several ways; as a lock, of course, as a game or toy, or as a demonstration of computer logic circuits. If used as a lock, the construction arrangement shown in Fig. 9-1 would probably not be satisfactory, because the combination could be discovered merely by opening the box and tracing the wiring. In addition, when used as a lock, instead of having a light flash when the proper combination has been found, some sort of electromechanical device, such as a solenoid, would be used to open a bolt.

When used as a game or toy, no changes are necessary, although you might wish to have a lamp glow when each section of the combination has been found. If by having one lamp lit he could see that he was making some progress, a player might be spurred on to a redoubled effort to light all three lamps. Such an arrangement is shown on the wiring diagram in Fig. 9-2.

ABOUT THE CIRCUIT

The logic lock circuit (Fig. 9-2) consists of mechanical AND and OR circuits. To get an output of a particular form

Fig. 9-1. Logic lock.

or nature in an AND circuit, all the circuit inputs must be of an identical nature. For example, to get an output of positive polarity (Fig. 9-3A), *all* the inputs must be of positive polarity. If *any* input is not positive, the output will not be positive. A mechanical equivalent of this logic can be seen in Fig. 9-3. If closing a switch is considered an input, it can readily be seen that only when all the inputs are present will an output be present. This is the case of the logic lock—instead of the inputs being positive or negative voltages, they are switches that are either closed or open. If you have no input (i.e., a switch set to an open contact) or to the wrong contact, then you will have no output.

In an OR circuit, *either* input being positive will cause a positive output. Fig. 9-4A shows the electron flow that causes the OR circuit to behave as it does. If the positive input to the top diode is 10 volts, then the output will be +10 volts.

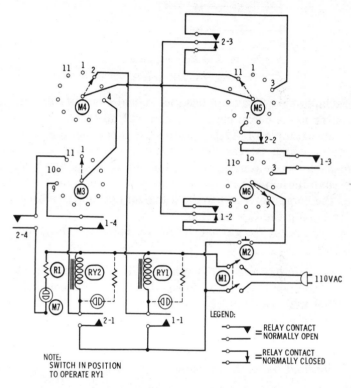

Fig. 9-2. Circuit diagram of logic lock.

If the input signal on *both* diodes is more negative than the negative potential at the bottom end of the resistor (resulting in both diodes being cut off), then the output will be negative. The mechanical analogy to this circuit can be seen in Fig. 9-4B. Here, either switch being closed will give an output equal to the input.

In digital computers, AND and OR circuits are as common as electrons; thousands of them appear in a computer of any

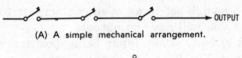

(A) A simple mechanical arrangement.

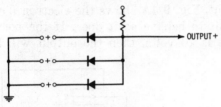

(B) A diode configuration.

Fig. 9-3. AND circuits.

appreciable size. They are used as logical elements to help the computer make decisions . . . if you will, to think.

As an example of AND circuits use, consider the case of a computer which is reading information from (or writing information on) magnetic tape when it senses a mark on the tape that indicates the end of the reel is very near. At this point the computer must make a logical decision; i.e., whether or not to stop the tape motion.

The computer is guided in its decision by the following factors:

1. Reading or writing? If reading, then tape motion cannot be stopped because to do so would leave unread information near the end of the tape.
2. Writing long, or short, groups of data on tape? If writing long groups of information on tape, to continue might mean writing off the end of the reel of tape, so tape motion had better be stopped.

A block diagram of this "thought" process as it takes place in an AND circuit might appear as shown in Fig. 9-5. Note

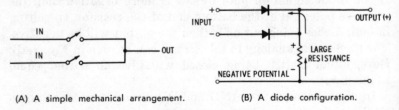

(A) A simple mechanical arrangement. (B) A diode configuration.

Fig. 9-4. OR circuits.

that according to the earlier definition of an AND circuit, if any of the inputs had been missing (i.e., minus) there would have been no output from the AND circuit. In the case shown, all three inputs are present (+), so there is an output (+). In other words the inputs:

end of tape approaching AND *writing* AND *long records*

all present simultaneously creates *stop tape motion.*

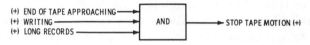

Fig. 9-5. AND circuit block diagram.

Other conditions could create the need for the OR circuits mentioned earlier. For example, if, during the reading or writing operation just described a fuse were to blow, the computer should be stopped at once, and the operator informed of the open fuse by an indicator light. Or, since computers are prone to error at high temperatures, if the temperature exceeds the safety limits, once again the computer should be stopped and the operator informed. Hence, to help the computer protect itself, an OR circuit such as that shown in Fig. 9-6 might be used. Here, since either condition is important enough to warrant stopping the machine, according to the definition of an OR circuit either *fuse blown* OR *temperature too high* can bring up the *halt* output and stop the computer. It is *not* necessary that both conditions be present at the same time to secure the *halt* output.

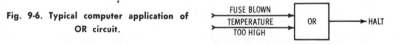

Fig. 9-6. Typical computer application of OR circuit.

In the logic lock exactly the same actions take place, except the conditions which make up the AND and OR circuits are created by rotary switches and relay contacts rather than diodes and resistors. Table 9-1 shows the combination to operate the logic lock when it is wired as shown in Fig. 9-2. The circuit that operates each part of the lock is as follows:

85

1. M2, M6-5, Ry1-2 n/c, Ry2-3 n/c, M5-11, M4-2, Ry1 coil.
2. M2, [(M6-3, Ry1-3 n/o, Ry2-2 n/c, M5-7) OR (M6-8, Ry1-2 n/o, Ry2-3 n/c, M5-11)], M4-4, M3-9, Ry1-4 n/o, Ry2 coil.
3. M2, M6-8, Ry1-2 n/o, Ry2-3 n/o, M5-3, M4-4, M3-11, Ry2-4 n/o, R1-M7 lamp combination.

In the second step, the circuit description enclosed in brackets represents a combination of AND and OR circuits. A diagram of this AND-OR combination is shown in Fig. 9-7. Note that selecting switch positions (M5-7) and (M6-8) will not cause an output because neither AND circuit has both inputs present at the same time. You can check the validity of this logic by setting up these conditions on the logic lock or by tracing it out on the wiring diagram.

Table 9-1. Logic lock switch positions.

M3	M4	M5	M6	Operated
*	2	11	5	Relay 1
9	4	7 or 11	3 or 8	Relay 2
11	4	3	8	Lamp M7

Incidentally, the form of diagram that is shown in Fig. 9-7 is exactly the same as those used by the maintenance technicians who serve the giant computers you read about—the only difference is in the degree. The technician is confronted with page after page of such diagrams as he follows a trouble through the machine.

CONSTRUCTION

The logic lock is constructed in a $3 \times 5 \times 7$-inch aluminum box. It operates from 115 volts AC supplied by the power cord shown on the left in Fig. 9-1. Be sure to use wire with insulation capable of withstanding at least 115-volts AC.

Before drilling any holes in the aluminum box, be certain that you have arranged all the parts to fit in the available space (Fig. 9-8). While there is room enough, there is none to spare, and a mistake at this stage of the project can make

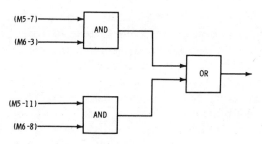

Fig. 9-7. AND-OR circuit combination.

it very difficult for you to complete construction to your satisfaction.

It is not necessary to use eleven-position switches in the construction—they were used in the original model because a local parts distributor happened to have a bin full of them for only 31 cents apiece. If instead he had had six-position

Fig. 9-8. Internal construction of logic lock.

switches "on special" for 25 cents each, then the logic lock would have six-position switches instead of those it has. This way of approaching the parts problem in this or any of the other projects is strongly recommended—for reasons of economy if no other. If used as a game, the logic lock should be constructed using four- or five-position switches as M3-M6. After all, the player should have *some* chance to win.

Don't forget that if you want the switches shown in Fig. 9-1 to turn clockwise going from 1 to 11, then you must wire them counting counterclockwise as viewed from the bottom.

Toggle switch M1 supplies power to the unit and also functions as a reset, dropping out the relays when opened. Pushbutton switch M2 is used to do the work of picking up the relays instead of the more delicate rotary-switch contacts. M2 should be depressed only after the rotary switches have been set to a combination—the rotary switches are then reset to a new combination, M2 is again depressed, and so forth (Table 9-1).

When you push M2, you *may* notice that the relay doesn't "pick up" quickly and smoothly with a click, as the armature seals to the core. If a "b-r-r-r-p" sound is heard, either for a short time or as long as M2 is depressed, the relay is being de-energized, or "dropped out," as it is being picked up—the noise is caused by the armature as it moves back and forth. Stopping this noise is merely a matter of relay contact adjustment. If you check Fig. 9-2, you will notice that each relay is picked up through one of its own normally closed contacts—the trouble comes when this contact opens too soon. It must remain closed long enough to transfer the contact (either Ry 1-1 or Ry 2-1) that keeps the relay energized once it has been picked up. If the normally closed contact (i.e., Ry 1-2 n/c) opens before the normally open contact (i.e., Ry1-1 n/o) closes, the relay loses its energizing voltage and drops back to its normal position. When contact Ry1-2 n/c closes again, this action is repeated, resulting in the buzzing noise described earlier.

To correct this trouble, form the contact straps so that just as the normally closed contact opens, the normally open contact closes, e.g., just when the Ry 1-2 n/c contact opens, the Ry 1-1 n/o contact should close. This will cause the relay to transfer with a sharp click, and remain firmly energized until reset.

Note that the use of a separate holding contact will permit a different adjustment from that described in Chapter 8, where the same contact was employed in both picking and holding the relay.

Parts List

Item	Description
R1	100K, ½-watt resistor
M1	DPST toggle switch
M2	SPST push-button switch, momentary contact
M3-M6	single circuit, 11-position rotary switch
Ry1, Ry2	4-pole, double throw relay, 110 VAC coil
M7	NE51 neon bulb and holder

Variation

One significant variation to the basic circuit of Fig. 9-2 would be the use of battery power. This would remove all dependence on outside power and necessitate the use of DC relays; if a solenoid is used, as mentioned earlier, it would also have to be DC operated.

CHAPTER 10

Battery Trickle Charger

In a computer, a great deal of DC power is needed to operate a wide variety of electromechanical devices—solenoids, relays, even indicator lamps. The supplies that furnish this power are not necessarily sophisticated, but are merely simple rectifier-capacitor combinations capable of delivering enormous amounts of fairly well regulated DC. The regulation these supplies offer is due chiefly to the very heavy load on them. This type of power supply, when properly designed, will operate for years with virtually trouble-free performance.

CONSTRUCTION

The trickle charger shown in Fig. 10-1 reflects the simplicity of the supply after which it is patterned. It is constructed in a 4 × 5 × 6-inch aluminum box that has several ½-inch holes drilled in the top and both sides to permit cooling air to circulate through the interior.

If you use a different type of silicon diode (e.g., one that has the heat sink connection on the cathode rather than the anode) you may reverse the diodes from the connection shown in Fig. 10-2. However, in doing so you will also reverse the polarity of the output voltage from that shown in the schematic diagram, so remember to reverse the capacitor connections also.

Transformer T2 (Fig. 10-2) is a surplus transformer that has a 36-volt, center-tapped secondary with a current rating

Fig. 10-1. Storage battery trickle charger.

of six to eight amperes. It is not necessary that you use a duplicate—an equivalent substitute could be made by wiring three 12.6-volt secondary windings in series. This, of course, makes quite a bulky assembly, and it is for this reason that it is strongly recommended that you get the transformers (T1 *and* T2) *before* you get a box to put them in. And don't be too hasty in buying either transformer—it is possible to get

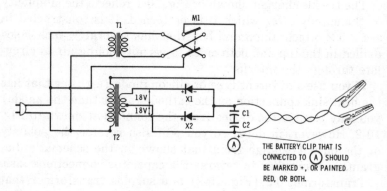

Fig. 10-2. Trickle charger circuit.

some real bargains in transformers if you can locate a dealer who has a stock of manufacturer over-production, or stock terminations. However, the general range of voltage and current ratings you will need are found in the Knight multitap selenium rectifier transformer (Allied stock #62G333).

T1 is a buck-boost transformer used to decrease or increase the charging rate. It is wired so that in *buck* position of switch M1, the voltage applied to the primary of T2 is reduced by 6.3 volts. That is, the secondary voltage of T1 is used to buck the primary voltage of T2 by a series-opposing connection.

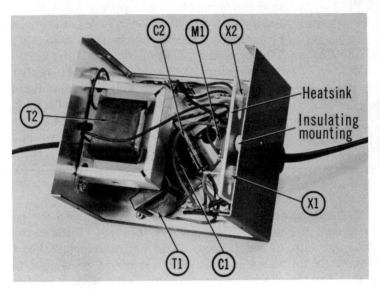

Fig. 10-3. Internal view of charger.

When the switch is placed in the *boost* position, the 6.3-volt secondary of T1 is connected in a series-aiding arrangement with the primary of T2, hence the two voltages add and the output of T2 is increased.

A ⅛-inch aluminum plate was used as a heat sink for X1 and X2 (Fig. 10-3). Two holes, each slightly smaller than the anodes of the rectifiers, were drilled into this plate, and then enlarged with a taper reamer (from both sides) to make a *tightly-fitting* connection to the rectifier anode. The plate was then mounted on a ceramic stand-off insulator. The electrical connection to the anodes is made by slipping a spade lug under the head of the screw that is used to fasten the plate to the stand-off insulator.

Parts List

Item	Description
C1, C2	Electrolytic capacitor, 250-mfd, 25 VDC
M1	DPDT toggle switch, 5-amp. contacts
T1	Transformer, 110 VAC prim., 6.3 VAC, 3-amp. sec.
T2	Transformer, 110 VAC prim., sec. (see text)
X1, X2	Silicon rectifier, *Delco* 1N3491R
Misc.	Battery clips (2), rubber feet (4) rubber grommets to fit ⅜-inch hole (2), aluminum box (see text), 5 feet of lamp cord with plug, 5 feet of heavy duty appliance cord, two 4-position terminal strips, 1-inch ceramic stand-off insulator or equivalent

USING THE TRICKLE CHARGER

To use the charger, connect the battery clip with the positive mark (+) on it to the positive terminal of the battery. The other clip, of course, goes to the negative terminal of the battery. If an ammeter is available it might be a good idea to measure the charging current—unless the battery is almost dead, the current should be somewhere between two and four amperes. The positive (+) terminal of the ammeter is connected to the + charger wire, and the negative (−) terminal of the ammeter is connected to the positive terminal of the battery. Use an ammeter capable of reading eight to ten amperes.

If the charging rate is too great (i.e., more than four amperes) a two- to five-ohm, 50-watt resistor can be connected in series with either one of the leads going to the battery. If the charging rate is too low, switch M1 should be placed in the boost position. Or perhaps the battery doesn't need charging.

CIRCUIT OPERATION

The circuit on which the trickle charger is based is called a full-wave rectifier, because the circuit components are arranged so the output current flows in the same direction during both halves of the AC input cycle.

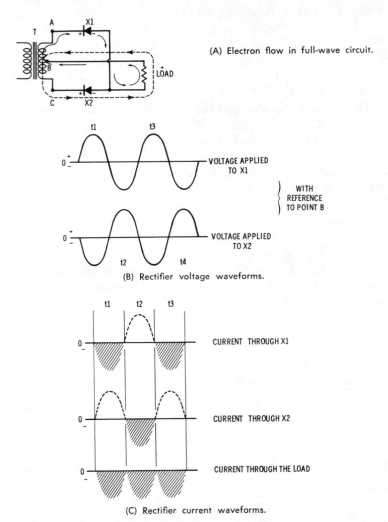

(A) Electron flow in full-wave circuit.

(B) Rectifier voltage waveforms.

(C) Rectifier current waveforms.

Fig. 10-4. Rectifier circuit principles.

The transformer (Fig. 10-4A) can be considered a source of voltage which has the shape shown in Fig. 10-4B. This voltage is impressed across X1 or X2 in series with the load resistor such that electrons will flow up through the load on each half of the AC cycle. For example, during time t1, the voltage applied to X1 is such that the cathode of the diode is positive with respect to its anode (reverse biased), so X1 will not conduct. However, during this same time the cathode of X2 is negative (Fig. 10-4C) with respect to its anode (forward biased), so that electrons flow through X2 and the load in the direction shown by the dotted line in Fig. 10-4A. At t2, the polarity of the wave has been reversed, X2 is reverse biased, and electrons flow through X1 (cathode negative with respect to anode) and the load resistance in the direction shown by the solid arrows in Fig. 10-4A. During t3, the polarity of the input voltage has again been reversed, X1 is cut off, and X2 conducts through the load.

An examination of the waveforms in Figs. 10-4B and C will show that only one diode is conducting at any given instant, and that each diode conducts such that the half cycle of voltage developed across the load is always of the same polarity.

In a full-wave rectifier (without a filter such as C1 and C2 in Fig. 10-2) with a sine-wave input, the average voltage is equal to .636 times the peak voltage of the applied wave. The rms voltage across the load is equal to .707 of the peak input voltage. The input voltage in a full-wave rectifier is the voltage between the center tap of the transformer (T) secondary, point B, and the ends of transformer T, points A or C.

CHAPTER 11

At Last—Perpetual Motion

Here is a project that, judging from the reaction to the original model, will furnish hours of enjoyment for persons of any age. There is something about machines that can capture and hold people's attention as nothing else can; especially machines that react to their environment. The perpetual motion machine—well, perhaps to be a *little* more accurate it should be called a reacting machine—uses the principle of feedback to change its state in response to a change in its environment.

Generally speaking, feedback is the utilization of all, or a portion of, the output signal of a device as all or a part of the input to that device. This process is one of the most essential in the operation of an analog computer, occurring especially in the operational amplifier, a precision DC feedback device used in performing basic arithmetic operations.

In the perpetual motion . . . oops, the reacting machine that is the object of this chapter, the feedback is mechanical and depends on the absence of light. That is, the output of the machine is light—delivered to the surface of a photocell. The feedback, 180° out of phase, is shade produced at the photocell by a light screen.

CONSTRUCTION

Perhaps the most important thing to remember in constructing the perpetual motion machine is what you are trying to do. This little machine is always trying to illuminate the photocell; your task is to control how often this is allowed to happen, and for how long.

This control is exercised by varying the rate of descent of the screen arm (Fig. 11-1) because as the light screen comes between the light source and the photocell, a critical point is reached where the photocell becomes (in effect) starved for light, and energizes relay M2. When this relay is energized, motor M3 begins to drive the operating/single-revolution cam assembly through a rubber-band drive belt. This has two effects; the single-revolution cam blocks the light from the photocell, thus making sure that the shaft makes one complete revolution, no more, no less! The second effect is that the operating cam raises the light screen from its block position. Therefore, when the opening in the single-revolution cam is aligned with the light source and photocell, relay M2 drops back to normal and the driving action ceases.

The next step is the most difficult. It consists of adjusting a screen-arm counterweight and/or the brake against the brake spool so that the light-screen arm descends very slowly, making the period between revolutions of the operating camshaft as long as possible. This is tricky because it involves adjusting two or three variables more or less simultaneously:

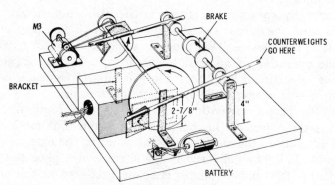

Fig. 11-1. Construction diagram of perpetual-motion machine.

1. The position of a counterweight weight on the end of the light-screen arm (on the opposite end from the screen).
2. The tension of the brake arm against the brake spool.
3. The weight on the long end of the operating cam follower arm. This weight may not be necessary; it should not be added unless you absolutely cannot get the action you want without it. The purpose of this weight is to reduce the delicacy of the brake arm adjustment and allow it to be performed with relative ease.

Single-revolution/Operating-cam Assembly

The single-revolution/operating cam assembly is constructed on a seven-inch shaft made from $\frac{5}{16}$-inch dowel rod (Fig. 11-2). The two spools on this shaft are glued into position so their ends are flush with the ends of the shaft. The drive spool should be as large as you can get (within reason) in order to increase the ratio between it and the drive pulley on the motor. This acts to reduce the speed with which the cam assembly turns as it is driven. The drive spool shown is $1\frac{3}{16}$-inch in diameter. Since the shaft will probably be larger than the hole through the spool, the latter will probably need to be enlarged with a rat-tail file.

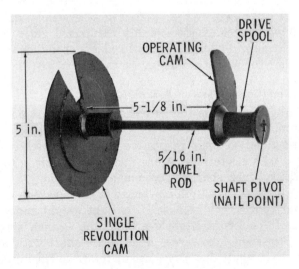

Fig. 11-2. Single-revolution / operating-cam assembly.

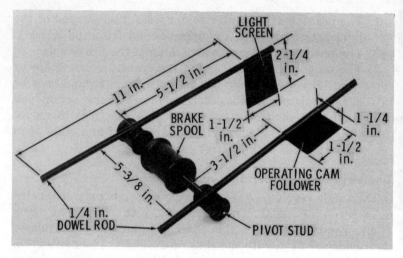

Fig. 11-3. Operating-cam follower/light-screen assembly.

A nail with the head removed is forced into a small hole drilled in each end of the shaft. Or you can pound a brad about one inch long into the shaft (be sure to get it straight!), leaving about ⅛-inch projecting. This projecting end can be filed to a point to make a fairly frictionless pivot.

The single-revolution cam is made of two layers of thick cardboard as shown in Fig. 11-2. The operating cam is also made of two layers of good quality cardboard glued together with the grain of one piece of cardboard perpendicular to that of the other for added strength.

Light-screen/Cam-follower Assembly

The light-screen/cam-follower assembly (Fig. 11-3) is fashioned from spools fastened to a $\frac{5}{16}$-inch dowel rod shaft. The arms are glued to their respective spools in notches filed in the spools by a rat-tail file. A one-inch brad is driven into each end of the $\frac{5}{16}$-inch shaft to serve as a pivot stud.

Thin (.015-inch) aluminum sheet is used as the cam follower and light screen because of its light weight and wearing qualities. It is formed tightly around the ¼-inch shafts; in addition, the cam follower is glued to its shaft with *Seal-All* compound (or equivalent) because of the frequent impacts between it and the operating cam.

The centers of the two arms are 5⅜-inches apart, and the arms are mounted on the main shaft at an angle of 7° to each other. That is, if the screen arm is held horizontal, the cam follower arm will be at an angle of 7° *above* horizontal.

The brake spool should be sanded as smooth as possible in the area where the brake will rub to prevent any binds due to roughness or cracks in the spool. (It was necessary to re-sand the spool shown in Fig. 11-3 after the photograph was made due to roughness caused by the paint.)

Drive Motor

The drive motor shown in Fig. 11-4 is manufactured by Victory Industries (Surrey) Ltd., Guildford, England. It has a pulley speed of 600 to 800 rpm at three to six volts DC. A broad rubber band, stretched between the M3 drive pulley and the drive spool, transfers power to the entire system. Some indication of the size of the motor is indicated by its relative size compared to the scale shown in Fig. 11-4.

The distance from the drive motor to the drive spool is quite critical; using a rubber band that measured 1½ inches without stretching, the best operation was secured when the motor pulley was 2½ inches from the center of the spool shaft. Careful experimenting may be necessary to achieve the proper distance if another length rubber band is used.

Fig. 11-4. Drive motor.

Electronic and Relay Assembly

The electronic chassis may be recognized as the unit constructed in Chapter 5 as a low-candlepower, self-switching night lamp. The changes made to adapt this unit for use in the perpetual motion machine consist solely of removing the lamp bulb and substituting a low-voltage DC relay (1½-to 3-volt DC, 100-ohm coil) having a SPST normally open contact (Fig. 11-5). The circuit for this application is shown in Fig. 11-6. The relay is mounted on the opposite end from where the lamp bulb was located, and the hole formerly filled by the bulb is used to bring out power leads and wires to the motor (M3). (Sufficient power for the entire machine can be supplied by a simple DC supply made from a 2½-volt filament transformer and a half-wave silicon rectifier.

Parts List

Item	Description
R1	47K, ½-watt resistor
X1	2N591 PNP transistor
X2	2N214 NPN transistor
X3	1N92 rectifier
M1	3-volt dry cell, or 3-volt power supply (see text)
M2	relay, SPST n/o contact, 100-ohm coil, to operate on 3 volts
M3	3-to-6 volt DC motor (see text)
PC	International Rectifier Corp. Type A15 photocell, or equivalent

SETTING UP THE MACHINE

The entire machine is assembled on a piece of ½-inch plywood, 12 inches on each side.

The shaft assemblies are mounted on right-angle brackets, as shown in Fig. 11-1, by inserting the pivot studs at the ends of the shafts into small depressions in the angle brackets. These depressions are about $\frac{1}{32}$-inch deep and $\frac{1}{16}$-inch in diameter; they are made by just starting a hole with a $\frac{1}{16}$-inch drill. The centers of the shafts are five inches apart; the

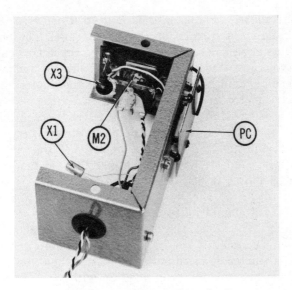

Fig. 11-5. Photocell amplifier chassis.

single-revolution/operating-cam shaft is mounted 2⅞ inches above the base; the light screen/cam follower assembly shaft is mounted four inches above the base.

The photocell/electronic assembly is fastened to the wooden base by the use of a small right angle bracket bolted to bot-

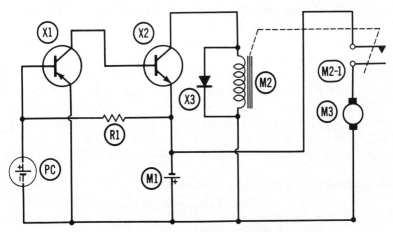

Fig. 11-6. Circuit diagram of amplifier.

tom of the chassis. The chassis is laid on its side so that the photocell and single-revolution cam are parallel. The photocell should be as close as possible to the single revolution cam.

A 1½-volt prefocused lamp located about 1½ inches from the photocell should be used to illuminate the photocell.

The drive motor is positioned about two inches on the opposite side of the drive spool from the light screen and cam follower shaft, and a rubber band is stretched between the drive spool and motor pulley. The polarity of the battery, or power supply, connections should be such that the motor drives the shaft as shown in Fig. 11-1.

The operation of the light, the drive motor, and single-revolution cam should be tested before going any further in the assembly. When operating properly, the motor should drive the cam continuously if the light is out, and stop driving the instant the photocell is illuminated (i.e., when the opening in the single revolution cam is lined up with the light and the photocell). If the light is shaded for a *short* time, the camshaft should make one revolution and stop.

The size of the opening in the single revolution cam is critical; if it is too small, when the cam jiggles about after stopping (due to the rubber-band drive) the cell may become shaded and cause the motor to drive for another cycle, or even two or three more; or perhaps the motor might run continuously. On the other hand, if the opening is too large, the machine may fail to make complete cycles without several jerky starts. Start with a wedge shaped opening about ⅝-inch wide at the outside edge of the cam, and proceed from there if further adjustment is necessary.

However, an effect similar to that caused by a too-narrow cam opening can also result from excessive tension on the rubber-band drive belt. Hence, if you experience multiple-cycle trouble, be sure to check drive belt tension. This tension is adjusted either by using a larger rubber band, or by moving the motor closer to or farther from the drive spool.

Counterweight and Brake Adjustment

There isn't a great deal that can be said about counterweight and brake adjustment—it's mostly just cut and try. However, after all the prior adjustments have been made, and the machine operates the light screen arm assembly in the proper manner, it's time to attach a small counterweight to the light screen arm. The counterweight can be a large machine nut or a few washers held in place temporarily with tape, while the adjustments are made. If the first try is close to the correct location, you'll notice that the arms don't flop down immediately after dropping off the high dwell of the operating cam, but rather descend a little more slowly. Continue to adjust the counterweight until the arm descends so slowly that eight to ten seconds occurs between cycles. You may find that when the arms are this delicately balanced, they tend to go too far up when lifted by the operating cam. In this case, use a piece of string (or any other method) to limit the upward travel.

If you're too impatient to try for such a delicate adjustment, add a *little* weight to the cam follower arm (Fig. 11-1) and use the brake to slow the arm descent.

The brake is a right angle bracket made of fairly thick iron so that it is stiff. Book shelf brackets are very good for this purpose—indeed, for all the brackets used in this machine. File a long slit in the brake bracket for mounting to the wooden base, so that it can be slid back and forth. This is how the brake tension is adjusted (i.e., the brake is touched against the brake spool with just enough tension to slow the rate of descent of the two arms). If you wish, you might glue a little strip of leather against the steel bracket where it touches the brake spool.

Use as little braking as possible, because this machine responds better to a delicate touch than to brute force. That is one of the nice things about the perpetual motion machine; you may find that you have a real talent for such delicate adjustment.

CHAPTER 12

The Sonolamp

The sonolamp is a sound operated lamp. It was originally designed to respond to the sound of a telephone bell; when the telephone rang the lamp was to light. Subsequent experiments however, showed that it was capable of considerably more than an occasional operation in the middle of the night. Indeed, it could be quite useful if it were never to be employed for that purpose. Bear in mind, though, if you receive frequent calls at night, the sonolamp can put an end to groping for light switches or stumbling about a dark room looking for the telephone.

What are some of the other uses? Well, suppose you discover that you are going to be out late some evening and you want to turn on a light in your house as a measure of burglar protection (strongly recommended by police officials)—you have merely to call your own telephone, let it ring a few times, then hang up. (If a strange voice answers you may have waited too long to make your call, and it is suggested that your next call be to the police.)

The sonolamp will operate very well with signals other than the telephone. If you ever come home after dark and your arms are loaded with packages, rather than sidle along the wall trying to flip the light switch with your shoulder or your elbow, whistle sharply, and the sonolamp will light at once. Another possible use is turning on the lights inside your garage with a beep of your auto horn.

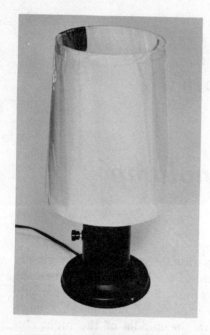

Fig. 12-1. The completed sonolamp.

Consider the possibilities if the relay in the sonolamp is used for something other than turning on a lamp. Now you have a switch that responds to sound, and anything that you could control with a manual switch, you can now control with sound.

If a suitable tuned circuit is used in the input to the sonolamp, it becomes much more selective in the frequencies to which it will respond, and much less responsive to random noise.

ABOUT THE CIRCUIT

Power and circuitry to operate relays is a necessary part of any large scale electronic computer. While it is fairly obvious that such a computer would contain many relays, it might not be at all obvious that the current needed to operate these relays (some of which might be 100 or more feet away from the central computer) could not very well be furnished by a central power supply due to the excessive power loss in long cables. Consequently the relay power is generated where it is to be used (with a simple low-voltage supply); the application of that power is controlled from a remote location. It is the principle of the control application that is used in the sonolamp.

The circuit used to operate a relay is called a *relay driver,* and is based upon the idea of completing a circuit when a transistor conducts, just as though a switch had been thrown. This is done by an arrangement such as that shown in Fig. 12-2. The relay power can be furnished locally, and the low power control signal can be brought to the transistor by cable. At long as the control signal applied to the base of the transistor is positive with respect to the emitter, the transister acts as an open circuit and the relay does not operate. When the control signal is negative, the transistor conducts and the relay operates.

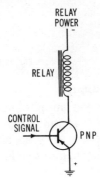

Fig. 12-2. Basic relay driver circuit.

The circuit of Fig. 12-2 is not the only form of relay driver. The same effect can be achieved by using an NPN transistor and reversing the polarities of the power source and control signal.

CONSTRUCTION

Construction of the sonolamp is best done in sections. With the completion of each, it can be tested to see if it performs as expected—if it does not, troubleshooting can begin at once.

There are four logical sections in the sonolamp; the power supply, the audio input and relay driver section, the relay section, and the lamp assembly.

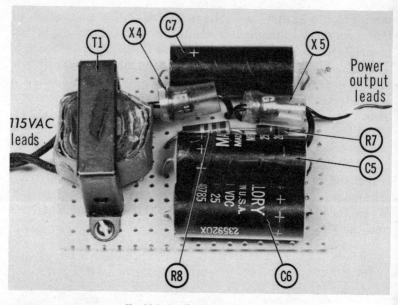

Fig. 12-3. Sonolamp power supply.

Power Supply

The power supply should be laid out as shown in Fig. 12-3, and wired as indicated in Fig. 12-4. All the connections are made on the reverse side of the $2\frac{7}{16} \times 3\frac{3}{8}$-inch perforated circuit board, and two leads about four inches long are attached

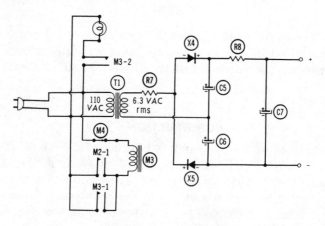

Fig. 12-4. Power supply circuit.

to carry the power to the audio input unit. The black leads on transformer T1 are the input to the 115-volts AC primary winding, the green leads are the 6.3-volts AC secondary output.

Be sure to use a heat shunt when soldering the germanium rectifiers into the circuit. While it is not necessary to test this section of the sonolamp, it may be done by temporarily wiring a 1000-ohm, 1-watt resistor in parallel with C7 and measuring the voltage; it should measure between 12 and 15 volts DC. Be sure to remove the resistor after testing.

Audio Input and Relay Driver

The audio input and relay driver section is also constructed on a $2\frac{7}{16} \times 3\frac{3}{8}$-inch perforated circuit board, as shown in

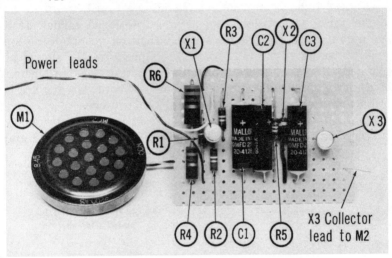

Fig. 12-5. Audio-amplifier/relay-driver board, and microphone.

Fig. 12-5. As in the power supply, all connections are made on the same side of the circuit board, so be certain to use insulating "spaghetti" over the bare component leads.

Note that the audio input circuit does not have a sensitivity control. If such a control is desired, add the components shown in Fig. 12-6 to the circuit. The wires going to potentiometer Rs should be long enough to allow the control to be easily mounted on the lamp base—six inches should be sufficient. You can always cut off or coil up the excess wires.

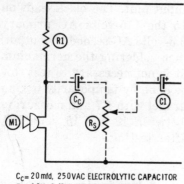

Fig. 12-6. Sonolamp sensitivity control.

C_C = 20 mfd, 250 VAC ELECTROLYTIC CAPACITOR
R_S = 10K, 1/2-WATT POTENTIOMETER

Fig. 12-7 shows one method of adding a tuned circuit to the input for greater selectivity, as was mentioned earlier. If it is to be used in conjunction with a sensitivity control, the top end of the tuned circuit (where it connects to C1) should be connected to the center tap of the sensitivity potentiometer. Suitable components for a 500-cps resonant circuit are a 10-mfd capacitor and a 10-millihenry inductance.

The audio input and relay driver section can be tested by connecting the X3 collector lead (Fig. 12-5) to relay M2 and

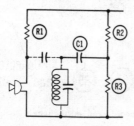

Fig. 12-7. Tuned circuit for added selectivity.

completing the power connections indicated in Fig. 12-8. The carbon microphone element is connected to the audio input circuit by soldering a wire to each of the silvery contact surfaces on the back side of the element (Fig. 12-9). When all the connections have been checked, connect the power supply cord to 115 volts AC and whistle into the microphone element. Relay M2 should pick up and remain so for about ½ second after the whistle has stopped. If you wish, sensitivity checks can be made at this time—don't forget to test the unit using a ringing telephone as signal. The unit should operate satisfactorily at least 12 to 18 inches away from the telephone. Remember that relay M2 will not remain transferred more than ½ second or so after the signal has stopped because there is no circuit to keep it energized. It will, however, be transferred long enough to pick up relay M3 (this happens almost instantly), and relay M3 *will* remain energized.

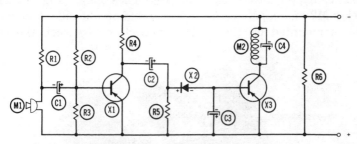

Fig. 12-8. Circuit of amplifier and relay driver.

Failure to operate relay M2 might be caused by insufficient output from the carbon microphone element. In the original sonolamp, it was necessary to try a second element before the unit would operate satisfactorily. The elements were obtained from a surplus outlet for 25 cents each (don't neglect this source when you shop for these and other parts).

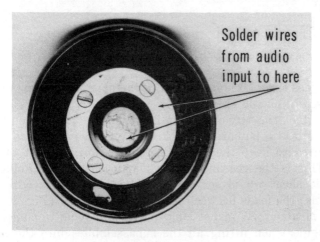

Solder wires from audio input to here

Fig. 12-9. Rear view of microphone.

After the unit has been tested to your satisfaction, the power supply and audio units are fastened together as shown in Fig. 12-10. The screws shown are 1 inch long. Be careful when you tighten the nuts lest you crack the circuit boards.

Relay Section

The relay section is constructed on a sheet of $\frac{1}{16}$-inch clear plastic, $3\frac{3}{16}$-inches wide, and $3\frac{1}{2}$-inches long (Fig. 12-11). Relay M2 and capacitor C4 are mounted on one side, and relay M3 is mounted on the other. Connections between the two

Fig. 12-10. Power supply mounted above audio board.

relays pass through holes drilled in the plastic, *not* around the sides of the plastic sheet.

Since the armature of relay M2 is connected to its mounting base (both at a potential of 115 volts AC), some means must be devised to keep the relay insulated from the rest of the unit. This is the reason for the plastic sheet—a bakelite or phenolic sheet would serve as well. Switch M4 is wired at this time; the leads between it and relay M3 coil (Fig. 12-11) should be about $3\frac{1}{2}$ inches long to give you room to maneuver and juggle when fitting all the subassemblies into the lamp base.

At this point—when all connections are properly made, power is applied, and an audio signal is furnished—correct operation is indicated if relay M2 picks up, followed instantly by relay M3. When the audio signal stops, M2 should be de-energized (drop out) in about ½ second, but relay M3 should

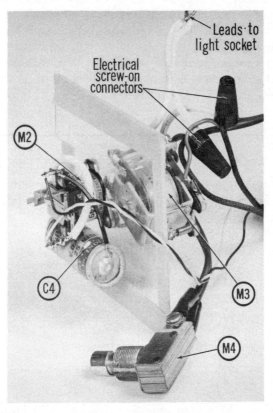

Fig. 12-11. Relay and reset switch assembly.

remain energized. When push-button switch M4 is depressed, relay M3 should drop out.

Lamp Assembly

The last step in the project is building the lamp assembly. Careful work in this part of the project will result in a lamp that is as handsome as it is useful. The lamp shown in Fig.

12-1 started out life as a fruit-juice can—$3\frac{5}{16}$ inches in diameter and $7\frac{1}{2}$ inches tall.

One end of the can is removed; a hole is drilled in the other end to admit the base of the light bulb socket. Two inches above the bottom (the open end) of the can, another hole is drilled to mount switch M4. The inside of the can is lined with some sort of insulating material; fishpaper, varnished cambric, or heavy cardboard. This is important. Although the unit has been designed so that the 115-volt circuits can not normally come into contact with the metal can, the insulating lining gives that extra margin of safety necessary when using commercial power (115 VAC or higher).

Parts List

Item	Description
C1, C2, C3	20-mfd, 25 VDC electrolytic capacitor
C4	100-mfd, 25 VDC electrolytic capacitor
C5, C6, C7	250-mfd, 25 VDC electrolytic capacitor
R1	1800-ohm, $\frac{1}{2}$-watt resistor
R2	220K, $\frac{1}{2}$-watt resistor
R3	10K, $\frac{1}{2}$-watt resistor
R4	5.6K, $\frac{1}{2}$-watt resistor
R5	15K, $\frac{1}{2}$-watt resistor
R6	1200-ohm, $\frac{1}{2}$-watt resistor
R7	47-ohm, $\frac{1}{2}$-watt resistor
R8	150-ohm, $\frac{1}{2}$-watt resistor
X1, X3	2N270 PNP transistor
X2	1N120 germanium diode
X4, X5	1N538 rectifier
M1	carbon microphone element
M2	1500-ohm sensitive relay, SPST contact
M3	relay; 115 VAC coil, DPDT contacts
M4	push-button switch, normally closed contact
T1	transformer; 115 VAC primary, 6.3 VAC sec.
Misc.	115-volt lamp bulb and socket, AC line cord, plug, 2 perforated circuit boards $2\frac{7}{16} \times 3\frac{3}{8}$-inches (available from Lafayette Radio, stock number MS-304), 2 electrical screw-on connectors.

The microphone element can be mounted in several ways, depending on its shape and size. One method is to glue a piece of soft spongy material to the side of the can near the top, and then glue the back of the microphone element to this material. This type of mounting tends to reduce false lamp turn-on due to vibration of the element. The sonolamp is very sensitive to physical vibration, so be sure to take this into account when mounting your microphone element.

For the lamp base, it may be far easier to use one that is ready-made than to try to design your own. The base shown in Fig. 12-1 was removed from a discarded pin-up lamp, and fastened to the open end of the fruit-can by three spade bolts. An even more satisfactory solution to the problem of finding a suitable base might be to buy a lamp that has a hollow area of sufficient size that the power, audio, and relay assemblies will fit into it. This can result in a sonolamp of professional appearance (however it also adds to the expense).

Bases *can* be made of wood; if you have access to a wood-working lathe, a really beautiful base can be turned. Or a simple square or circular base can be cut and polished from small pieces of the more exotic hardwoods at very little expense.

The fruit-juice-can lamp body is painted a flat black (sometimes called a wrought iron finish) using a small can of spray paint. Be sure to follow the directions on the can.

CIRCUIT OPERATION

Voltage variations resulting from the action of audio energy on the carbon mike are coupled to the base of X1 through capacitor C1. Electron flow is from the negative terminal of the power source, through R1 and M1; also into the negative terminal of capacitor C1. Electrons then flow out of the positive terminal of C1 through R3 to the positive power terminal. This action causes a more negative potential to appear at the base of X1 (the base is very slightly negative due to the voltage divider action of bias stabilization network R2 and R3, forward biasing this transistor; electrons flow into its base and the transistor goes into conduction. Since the signal applied to M1 varies at an audio rate, so does the action just described. Hence, the signal voltage developed at the collector of X1 (by the electron flow through R4 and X1) is an amplified version of the audio input signal.

Through the usual capacitive charge and discharge action, the audio signal is coupled to the half-wave rectifier and filter formed by X2 and C3; i.e., *charging* electrons flow into C2 through R4, and out of C2 through R5; *discharging* electron flow is out of the negative terminal of C2, through the X2 collector-emitter circuit and through R5 back to the positive terminal of C2. Only negative-going alternations are felt at C3 (and the base of X3). C3 acts as a sort of electronic bucket into which electrons are poured on the negative cycles of the audio signal, and out of which they are poured in an effort to keep X3 conducting when the negative signal ceases. The action of C3, then, is to keep X3 conducting more or less continuously in spite of the fact that signal is present only about half the time. Of course, when X3 conducts, M2 is operated (picked up).

The purpose of C4 is very similar to that of C3—transistor X3 stops conducting between pulses and relay M2 tries to drop out (especially at the lower frequencies, where the time between negative pulses is greatest), C4 pours out its electrons through M2 coil to keep it picked up. When the signal stops (and the transistor current through the relay stops), C4 discharging through the relay coil will keep the relay energized for an appreciable period.

When relay M2 is operated, its normally open contact will transfer and pick up M3. This relay keeps itself energized through one of its own n/o contacts in series with its coil and 115 volts AC. To open the "hold" circuit and drop out relay M3, normally closed push-button M4 must be depressed.

Power Supply

The sonolamp power supply is a form of voltage doubler circuit. It operates by charging two capacitors to the peak voltage of the AC input signal (6.3 volts rms, in this case) and then placing them in series across the load. This is done in the following manner.

During a cycle of the alternating voltage present at the output of T1, electrons will flow through R7 (a surge-limiting resistor used to protect the diodes), then through C6, and back to the other end of the transformer. Since X5 is conducting, its resistance is very low and nearly the entire peak voltage of T1 (about 8.8 volts) is felt across C6.

During the reverse half-cycle alternation, electrons flow into C5 on one (negative) plate, out of the other (positive) plate through forward-biased diode X4. Since X4 is conducting, almost the entire AC voltage is felt across C5, so that at the end of one complete cycle, C5 and C6 (each charged to the transformer voltage) are connected in series across the load.

The no-load DC output of this supply is 2.82 times the input rms value, or about 18 volts. At the load imposed by the sono-lamp, the voltage is about 14 volts.

Capacitor C7 and resistor R8 serve to filter the ripple content in the rectified power supply voltage.

CHAPTER 13

The Black Box

Although it may appear so, the idea behind the black box is not to see how much can be crammed into a small box. This little device can be quite a puzzle to persons who pick it up for the first time, and try to light the lamp. Actually, their chances for lighting the lamp are one in six (there are six possible ways to press two of the four buttons) on the first try. And if you pass the black box around in a circle at a party—and change the combination each time you get your hands on it—very likely there'll be some people who will swear that it doesn't work, 'cause they never did get the lamp to light. Of course this is true only if they get but one try at a time, and if the lucky ones in the circle don't show the combination to anyone else.

The black box (actually it's gray) is handy for choosing partners at parties—the first two people who find the combination are partners, then the second pair, and so forth. If you really want to make it tough, don't tell anyone that two buttons must be depressed at the same time to cause the lamp to light.

Incidentally, this device is not limited to lighting a lamp; the relay contacts can be used to control any sort of apparatus that is within their contact rating (about ½ ampere). This should open the door to all sorts of control possibilities.

The black box can also serve as an excellent example of computer circuitry for demonstration purposes. The diode matrix around which the device is built is quite commonly used in translation circuits of electronic computers. Translators are the circuits used to convert the binary arithmetic used by the computer in solving problems into the decimal arithmetic form with which the operator of the computer is familiar, and which you commonly use everyday.

ABOUT THE CIRCUIT

One of the most interesting circuits in an electronic computer is the one which the computer central processing unit (the device that makes the decisions) employs to choose which unit of the system to use. For example, suppose that the computer has finished an arithmetic problem and desires to write

Fig. 13-1. The black box.

out the answer so that the operator can read it (or use it in some other fashion). To do this, the computer selects a printer or typewriter and tells it to print or type out the answer which has been produced by the arithmetic circuits.

However, since there may be more than one type of output unit (printers and typewriters are some examples of output units) available to the central processing unit, some means of differentiating between them is necessary if the proper unit is to be selected.

As an example of how this might be done, consider the case of a computer that has two flip-flops (Fig. 13-2) which are to be used for selecting output units. Call these flip-flops A and B. Their outputs, then, would be either A or $\overline{A}$ (read as not A), and B or $\overline{B}$. You can have either one or the other of these outputs simultaneously, but not both of them. That is, you

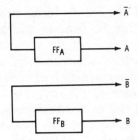

Fig. 13-2. Select unit flip-flops.

can have either A *or* $\overline{A}$, and either B or $\overline{B}$, but not both A *and* $\overline{A}$ or B *and* $\overline{B}$.

If these two outputs could be combined in just the right fashion, four separate results could be obtained (Fig. 13-3); four outputs from two inputs. So at this point, a "select output unit" circuit could be devised by letting AB stand for a printer, $A\overline{B}$ for a typewriter, $\overline{A}B$ for a magnetic tape unit, and $\overline{A}\overline{B}$ for a card punching machine (Fig. 13-4). All that it is necessary for the central processing unit to do to select any one of four units is to manipulate flip-flops A and B so as to obtain the desired output. One of the nice things about this circuit is that you can never select more than one unit at a time by accident, because it is not possible to have more than one output at any given time. (That is, unless something breaks down—which happens in computers more often than manufacturers like to think.)

Those who are interested in the contents of the black box will find more detail in the Circuit Operation section.

CONSTRUCTION

After you have made certain that you have all the necessary parts, the first step in the construction of the black box is building the subassemblies. Fig. 13-5 shows the arrangement of resistors R1 through R8, and switches M3 through M6.

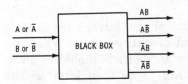

Fig. 13-3. Outputs of the black box.

This "pre-assembly" of resistors and switches is recommended because of the ease with which it can be done in the early stages of construction.

Fig. 13-6 shows the completed diode sub-assembly. Considerable pains should be taken in the construction of this part of the black box, as it is the very heart of the unit. Be especially careful when soldering the diodes to the terminals. To keep from overheating the diodes a heat shunt should be clipped between the diode and the terminal while soldering. A satisfactory heat shunt can be made by wrapping a rubber band several times across the handles of your needle-nose pliers so that the tips are tightly pressed together, just as though you were squeezing the handles in your hand, and then clipping the plier tips between the diode and the heat source while soldering.

The terminal boards shown in Fig. 13-6 were used because of their small size and convenience. Be sure to get boards with ten terminals each, for although only 16 of the 20 terminals are used for mounting the diodes, three of the remaining four are used for connecting the leads of the 2N214 transsistor (X9) into the circuit. While assembling the diode unit, be careful to point all the diodes the same direction. The end of the diode with all the stripes around the body is the cathode

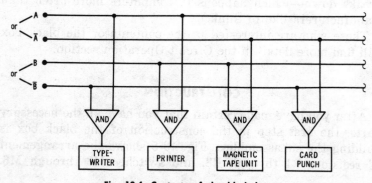

Fig. 13-4. Contents of the black box.

end. In Fig. 13-6, the cathodes are shown toward the bottom of the picture, as is the diode unit mounting screw. When the unit is mounted on the chassis, the anode leads should be away from the chassis, because they are to be used later as the output points of the diode matrix. This output connection is made with a small alligator clip, as shown in Fig. 13-7.

After the diodes have been soldered into place on the subassembly, they should be tested to be certain that they were not damaged during assembly. This can be done with an ohm-

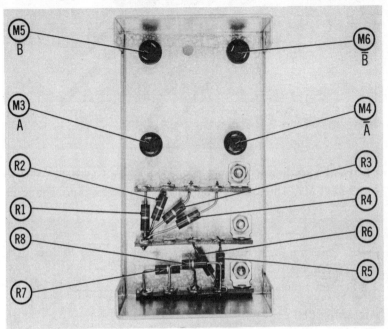

Fig. 13-5. Resistor and switch subassembly.

meter, using the ×100 scale—with the meter leads across the diode terminals, a reading of about 300 to 400 ohms should be obtained. When the leads are reversed, only a barely perceptible movement of the meter needle should be noticed. Do not worry if you can't see any meter needle deflection in the latter test, this merely means that the back resistance of the diode is too high to register on the ×100 scale, and that's good. It is not absolutely essential that this test be made, but it is going to be much easier at this time to remove any diodes that were damaged by heat or rough treatment than it is at any future step in the construction.

The remainder of the construction should be done in the following general order:

Fig. 13-6. Diode subassembly.

1. Drill the mounting holes for the power switch (M10), relay M7, the battery-mounting brackets, and the #49

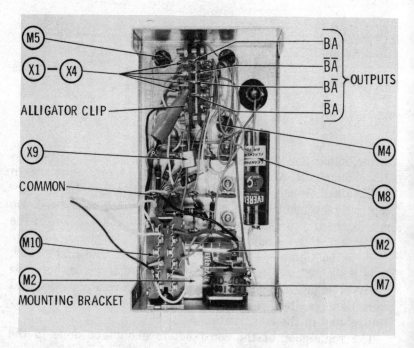

Fig. 13-7. Details of completed wiring.

lamp bulb (a ½-inch hole). Be careful in your location of the parts, as you have a lot of circuit to build into a small space.

2. Mount the 9-volt battery (M2).
3. Connect the wiring from the diodes to the resistors. Note (Fig. 13-7) that the insulation on *one* of the wires going to each of the diode anodes is removed and the two wires directly opposing are twisted together and then soldered, quickly. This is the output connection mentioned earlier.
4. Mount the relay, the power switch, and the battery holders (Fig. 13-8 shows the mounting of M1 and M9 on the side of the chassis bottom cover), and wire them into the circuit according to Fig. 13-9. (The relay is a unit out of a radiosonde weather unit. However, any relay

Fig. 13-8. Method of mounting batteries on bottom cover.

that will operate on about 2 or 3 volts, and has a coil resistance of about 100 ohms should do.) In this application, the relay is insulated from the chassis base by plastic screws and standoffs. It could also be mounted by first mounting it on a piece of plastic, and then mounting the plastic on the box. Be certain to install a diode across the relay coil with the polarity shown in Fig. 13-9.
5. Mount the 2N214 transistor as shown in Fig. 13-7.
6. Add any remaining parts, such as the alligator clip, and lamp bulb. The bulb is first pushed into the grommet as far as the glass envelope, then the grommet is pressed (a little at a time) into the ½-inch hole. Incidentally, although the lamp shown in Fig. 13-1 is not a No. 49 bulb, the latter should be used for a more positive indication with the 1½-volt cell, M8.

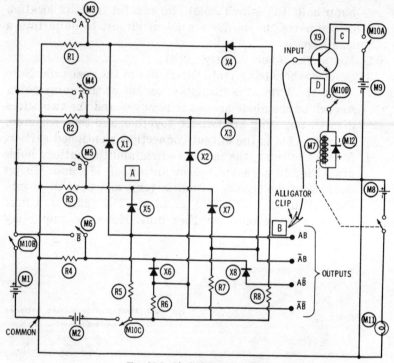

Fig. 13-9. Black box schematic.

7. CHECK YOUR WIRING. If you are satisfied that the unit is wired according to Fig. 13-9, you may insert the batteries.

Turn the unit on, and then start pressing buttons until you find the two that will light M11. If M11 fails to light, check to see if the relay operates. If the relay fails to operate, voltmeter checks of the circuit are in order. The voltmeter (VTVM) readings given in Table 13-1 were made with respect to the point marked COMMON on Fig. 13-9.

CIRCUIT OPERATION

The number of outputs from a logic matrix is equal to 2^N, where N is equal to the number of inputs to the matrix. The basic circuit in the black box is a two-input logic matrix;

therefore you would expect 2^2, or four, outputs, and this is what you will get. In order to do this, four AND circuits comprising two elements (or diodes) each are used. AND circuits, you will recall, are circuits which have one output for several (two in this case) inputs. That is, a signal must be present at each input to secure an output. In the black box, these four AND circuits are formed by diodes X1 and X5, X2 and X6, X3 and X7, and X4 and X8, respectively.

To make the circuit easier to understand, assume for a moment that the diodes are not in the circuit shown in Fig. 13-9. If switch M10C were closed, +9 volts would be present at each of the four output terminals. The circuits are then open, no current flows to cause a voltage drop across the 22K resistors, and the full battery potential appears at the output terminals.

Table 13-1. Voltmeter readings.

UNIT ON No Buttons Depressed		UNIT ON Buttons Pressed—Light On	
Point	Voltage	Point	Voltage
A	0.4	A	4.4
B	0.4	B	3.0
C	4.5	C	3.0
D	0.3	D	2.7

But with the diodes in the circuit, and wired as shown (forward biased), most of the voltage would be dropped across the 22K resistors. Only the drop across the very low diode forward resistance in series with the 560-ohm resistor (about 0.4 volt) appears at the output terminals. It is important to understand that a forward-biased (i.e., conducting) diode acts almost like a piece of wire in the circuit—whatever voltage appears on the cathode also appears on the anode. Hence the anode voltage is tied to (or clamped to) the cathode potential. This means that to raise the anode potential, it must be done by raising the clamping level, or cathode potential.

The flow of electrons which causes this action is from the negative terminal of the 9-volt battery (M2), through the

Parts List

Item	Description
R1, R2, R3, R4	560 ohm, ½-watt resistor
R5, R6, R7, R8	22K, ½-watt resistor
M1, M9	4.5-volt battery (Eveready No. 333, or equivalent)
M2	9.0-volt battery (Eveready No. 216, or equivalent)
M3, M4, M5, M6	SPST push-button switch, momentary contact
M7	SPDT Relay, 100-ohm coil res. (See text)
M8	1.5-volt cell (Eveready No. 915, or equivalent)
M10A, B, C, D	4PST slide switch (4PDT shown in Fig. 13-7)
M11	#49 pilot lamp
M12	1N120 diode
X1 through X8	germanium computer diodes (See text)
X9	2N214 NPN transistor
Misc.	Small alligator clip, terminal strips, battery holder (two types—for M2, and M1 and 9), metal box—3 × 5¼ × 2⅛-inches (Bud CU-2106-A, or equivalent), wire, nuts, and screws.

560-ohm resistors, through the diodes from cathode to anode, then through the 22K resistors and into the positive terminal of M2. It can easily be seen that since the only large resistances in these circuits are the 22K resistors, nearly all the potential drop occurs across them. The original conditions, then, are that all the diodes are conducting, and the potential at each of the four output terminals is nearly zero.

In order to cause a positive potential to appear at one of the output terminals (e.g., the AB terminal) plus inputs must be applied to the cathodes of the two diodes in the AND circuit connected with that output; i.e., X1 and X5. This is done by closing switches M3 and M5, causing a flow of electrons through R1 and R3 such that the 4.5-volt potential of battery

M1, is developed across each of these resistors. Since the positive (with respect to COMMON) ends of R1 and R3 are connected to X1 and X5 cathodes, the cathodes are raised to +4.5 volts. However, since X1 and X5 cathodes are still negative with respect to their anodes, these diodes are still forward biased (hence acting as virtual short circuits) and the plus 4.5-volt signal felt on the cathode is also felt as the anode, and consequently at the output terminal.

The electron flow which causes this output is exactly the same as that described earlier, except that 4.5 volts of the applied 9 volts is dropped across resistors R1 and R3 due to the bucking voltage of M1. Hence, only a 4.5-volt potential is felt across R5 instead of the entire 9 volts as in the previous example. This means that output terminal AB is at a potential of +4.5 volts instead of nearly zero as in the condition described earlier.

Note, however, that both M3 and M5 must be closed at the same time for this action to take place. If only one of these two switches is closed, raising only one diode cathode to +4.5, the other diode will still continue to clamp the output terminal to approximately zero. This is the basic AND circuit action—either input can keep the output down, but both are needed to raise it up.

The relay and transistor circuit used as an indicator is a simple emitter follower. This circuit is used because of its high input impedance. A low impedance load on the AND circuit can degrade the circuit action to the point where the difference between signal and no-signal levels is no longer distinguishable.

CHAPTER 14

Puzzle Box

This project is for the kids, or one for a rainy day. To keep small children amused for long periods, just build this simple toy for them, teach them how to use it, and set back and listen to the quiet. The idea, of course, is to have one child set the combination, and allow another to try to solve it and light the lamp. It is not *too* difficult to solve, being merely a matter of trying possible combinations until the right one is "hit." There are only 128 possible combinations, so eventually the children will find it. That's when a new combination is set up.

ABOUT THE CIRCUIT

The circuit (Fig. 14-1) is based on the principle of the AND circuit, which has been discussed previously in these pages, that

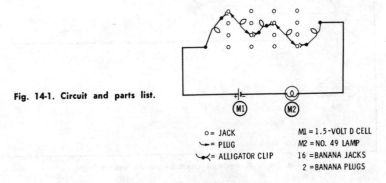

Fig. 14-1. Circuit and parts list.

o = JACK
⌐ = PLUG
⌐◄ = ALLIGATOR CLIP

M1 = 1.5-VOLT D CELL
M2 = NO. 49 LAMP
16 = BANANA JACKS
2 = BANANA PLUGS

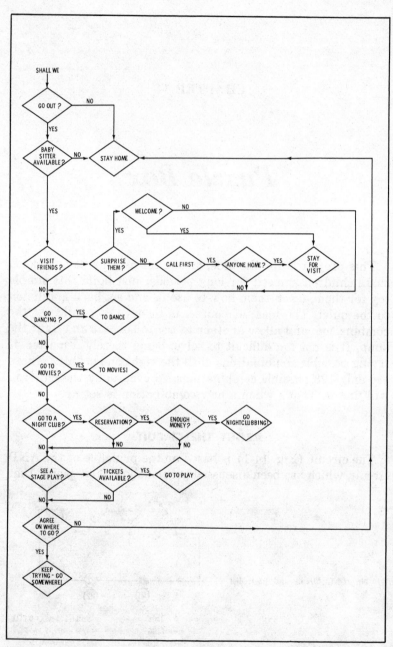

Fig. 14-2. A decision chart based on yes-no logic.

of obtaining a logical 1, or yes, output only when each input is a logical 1, or yes. This is exactly what is done here—the bulb lights a yes output, when all the yes inputs are present.

The basis for this and other similar circuits is a form of logic founded on binary, or two-valued, mathematics rather than the decimal mathematical basis with which you are familiar. In the binary form of mathematics an answer will be either yes or no, a voltage is either present or absent, a switch is either on (closed) or off (open).

Although it might appear that this form of logic would be so limited as to be virtually useless, consider the diagram in Fig. 14-2 as an example of the wealth of accomplishment achieved by only yes-no decisions. This diagram, incidentally, bears a marked resemblance to the "flow charts" used by computer programmers to get a clear understanding of the overall problem prior to writing instructions for the machine to perform.

CONSTRUCTION

The construction of the puzzle box consists mostly of drilling the holes for the jacks—be sure to use a center punch so

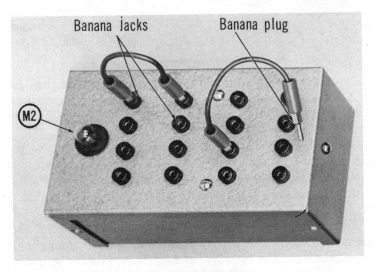

Fig. 14-3. The puzzle box.

the drill point won't wander all over the top of the box as the holes are being drilled. This is a good place to borrow a friend's drill press if you can. Fig. 14-3 shows the appearance of the completed toy from the outside, as well as the type of plug used. Be sure to try your plugs and jacks for "fit" before you buy them. Fig. 14-4 shows the inside of the chassis box and the method of selecting a combination. One of the alligator clip insulating sleeves has been removed to give some idea of the alligator clip size compared to that of the jacks.

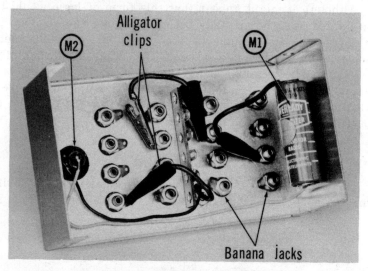

Fig. 14-4. Internal construction of puzzle box.

The battery shown at the top of the photo is held in place by a clamp fashioned from the strap material TV servicemen use to mount antennas on posts or poles. This material is fairly strong, yet easily worked.

One of the nice things about this project is that the parts (at least, the jacks) are not changed in any way due to their being used. If you need a jack for use elsewhere, you have merely to remove one from the puzzle box (if the kids will let you have it).

Remember to make the wires short enough to prevent jumping across the two middle rows of jacks, that is, plugging one end of a wire in the first row, and the other end in the last row, because that's just what children will do if they can.

CHAPTER 15

Regulated Power Supply

Regulated power supplies are used in both analog and digital computers to prevent sudden or excessive voltage variations.

In an analog computer, such a change would appear as another varying signal to be processed in the normal way, hence leading to erroneous output.

In a digital computer, abrupt voltage variations, or voltage changes in excess of certain limits (normal plus or minus approximately 10%) will cause either extraneous pulses to appear in the machine or normal pulses to drop out; either condition will lead to false results. Hence, the need for power supplies capable of good regulation can easily be seen.

These regulated supplies are normally used to furnish DC voltages to vacuum tubes or transistors, with power for relays and other mechanical devices being supplied by heavily-bled unregulated supplies. In a large scale computer the total demand for regulated current might run to several hundred amperes.

One thing all power supplies have in common is internal resistance. This resistance, acting in series with the load, will cause fluctuations in voltage when changes in either load or AC input occur. Since there is presently no way of eliminating this bane of good regulation, some means of working around it must be found.

The way this is accomplished in the power supply shown in Fig. 15-1 is to start out with a lot more voltage than is necessary, and then drop the excess across yet another resistance in series with the load. *This* resistance, however, is one whose value can be varied almost instantly, so that at all times the load on the power source can be kept constant. That is, if the value of the load resistance goes down, the value of the series resistance will go up, resulting in a constant load on the voltage source.

Fig. 15-1. The completed regulated power supply.

CONSTRUCTION

The regulated power supply pictured in Fig. 15-2 is constructed in an $8 \times 6 \times 3\frac{1}{2}$-inch aluminum box, using the circuit of Fig. 15-3A. If you wish to use the bridge rectifier circuit (Fig. 15-3B), transformer T should have a 24-to-26-volt AC secondary, and all four of the rectifiers should be 1N536 silicon units. The bridge rectifier should be hooked into the regulator circuit at the points marked A.

The holes visible in the top of the power supply are for cooling. Similar holes should be drilled in the bottom to promote a free flow of air.

After all the holes were drilled the unit was sprayed with a flat black paint—both for appearance and to improve the heat radiating properties. Be sure to cover the area on which the transistor is to be mounted with masking tape before spraying.

The transistor shown in Fig. 15-1 is a "junk box" transistor with a current gain of 60. Good results can also be had using a 2N277—it has slightly higher gain and more than adequate current capability. Also suitable are the 2N375, 2N376, 2N561, 2N618, to mention just a few.

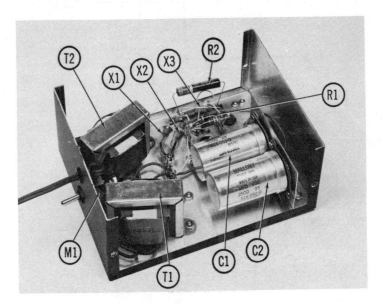

Fig. 15-2. Parts layout in power supply chassis.

No matter which transistor you use, be sure to use the proper type of insulating wafer to keep the transistor collector from touching the chassis. Also make the chassis as smooth as possible. Rub a fine grade of flat file across the area where the transistor is to be positioned, and coat both sides of the insulating wafer with a thin film of heat conducting grease of the type mentioned in Chapter 2.

Capacitors C1 and C2 are insulated from the chassis because the series connection (used to divide the supply voltage across these two capacitors) places a potential on the can. Also, this enables the user to ground either terminal of the output connections. Fig. 15-2 shows the capacitors mounted on the insulating phenolic plates, these in turn raised off the aluminum mounting bracket by fiber washers. Fig. 15-4 shows the details of C1 and C2 mounting.

The use of two capacitors in series (two equal capacitors acts to make one capacitor of half the capacitance value and twice the voltage rating) can be avoided by the use of a 1000-

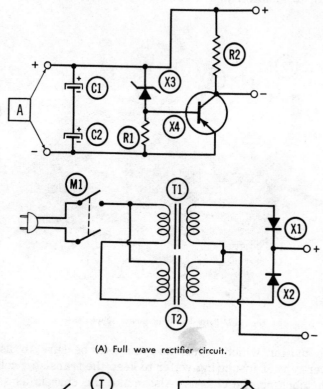

(A) Full wave rectifier circuit.

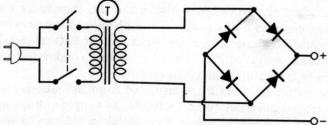

(B) Alternate transformer arrangement, with bridge rectifier circuit.

Fig. 15-3. 12-volts DC, 0.5-amp power supply.

mfd, 50-volt DC capacitor. C1 and C2 were used because they were on sale at reduced prices.

R1 is made up of three 3300-ohm, 1-watt resistors wired in parallel. R1 serves to limit current flow through zener diode X3.

CIRCUIT OPERATION

The rectifier portion of the power supply shown in Fig. 15-3A is essentially the same as that discussed in Chapter 10. The alternate circuit shown in Fig. 15-3B is a different type of full-wave rectifier known as a *bridge*. In this type of circuit the AC input is applied to two opposite corners of the diode

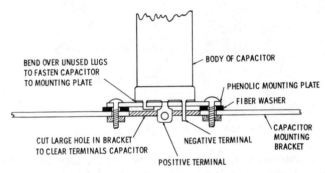

Fig. 15-4. Technique for mounting electrolytic capacitor.

network, and the pulsating DC output is taken from the remaining two corners. One advantage of the bridge rectifier is that it delivers almost twice as much output voltage as the full-wave circuit. This is because in the full-wave circuit the maximum voltage across the rectifier and load is that measured from the center tap to either end of the transformer. In the bridge circuit, however, there is no center tap, and the entire secondary voltage is impressed across the rectifiers and the load.

This action can be seen in Fig. 15-5; when the AC input potential on point A of transformer T is negative with respect to point B, electrons flow through X1, R, and X2 in the direction of the solid arrows. Since X1 and X2 are forward biased, their resistance to the flow of electrons is low, and nearly all the transformer voltage is impressed across R.

When the AC input voltage reverses, and point B is negative with respect to point A, electron flow is in the direction indicated by the dotted arrows. In both cases the voltage across R (the load resistance) is of the same polarity.

The voltage regulator shown in Fig. 15-3A is a *series* circuit, using a transistor for the variable resistance in series with the load. So that the transistor will have a reference about which to operate, a resistor (R1) and zener diode (X3) are used to tie the base of X4 to a nominal −12 volts. Any variation in the input voltage to the regulator, or in the load

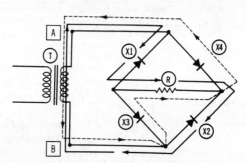

Fig. 15-5. Current flow in bridge rectifier.

current, will cause a variation in the X4 base-to-emitter voltage, hence changing the base current, and consequently the collector-to-emitter resistance. The net effect of this action is such that the output voltage never departs more than a few millivolts from −12 volts.

In a balanced condition, using the + terminal of the supply as a reference, −37 volts is measured at the X4 collector, −12 volts at the X4 emitter, and −12.2 volts at the base. This small potential between base and emitter (−.2 volt) causes a base current to flow and establishes the value of resistance between the X4 emitter and collector under static conditions.

However, if the voltage delivered by the rectifier were to increase (become more negative), then the voltage across X4 and R2 would also tend to become greater, and the output voltage would rise. But as the output becomes more negative, the potential between the base and emitter gets smaller (since the base is tied to the zener diode potential, −12.2 volts in this unit), less base current flows, and the collector-to-emitter resistance increases. The amount of this increase depends on the current gain of the transistor. This is because the small decrease in base current causes a greatly amplified decrease in collector current, and a consequent large increase in collector-to-emitter resistance. Therefore, the voltage across R2 will increase only a few millivolts; the reset of the increased supply voltage is developed across the increased resistance of the transistor.

But what if the rectifier supply voltage decreases (i.e., becomes more positive)? In this case, the base-to-emitter voltage becomes greater, and an increased base current will flow. With an increase in base current comes a greatly increased collector current, and a much smaller transistor resistance. Hence less of the rectifier supply voltage is dropped across X4, and more across R2, bringing the voltage back to its proper value.

Parts List

Item	Description
C1, C2	2500-mfd, 25 VDC, electrolytic capacitor.
R1	1100-ohm, 3-watt resistor (see text)
R2	150-ohm, 2-watt resistor
X3	1N1773 zener diode, 12-volt, 1-watt
X4	power transistor; 2N375, 2N376, 2N561, 2N618 or equiv.
X1, X2	1N537 silicon rectifier
T1, T2	transformer, 110 VAC prim.; sec. 24-26 VAC @ 2 amp
M1	DPST toggle switch
M2	2-position barrier strip
Misc.	Rubber grommets; aluminum box, 8 × 6 × 3½-inches; rubber feet; 3-position terminal strips (3), phenolic capacitor mounting plates (2), fiber washers (4).